Ed MacNab

The Alien-spotter's Handbook

Illustrations by Brian Howard-Heaton and John Higgins

An Armada Original

The Alien-spotter's Handbook was first published in
Armada in 1982 by Fontana Paperbacks,
8 Grafton Street, London W1X 3LA.
This impression 1983

Printed in Great Britain by
William Collins Sons & Co. Ltd., Glasgow.

Contents

Foreword

This is a reproduction of the last photograph to be taken (by a human being) of Dr. Thaddeus Qwax, the greatest Alien Spotter of them all . . .

Disguised as an ordinary, fun-loving schoolboy, Dr. Qwax was about to enter an amusement arcade, somewhere in London, in pursuit of the extra-terrestrial Mastermind, which, he believed, was controlling and directing the operations of Alien Saboteurs throughout the British Isles.

As we now know, it was the final mission of his long and distinguished career, for nothing has been seen or heard of Dr. Qwax since that fateful day. Fortunately, his extensive notes on Alien Activity have survived. In the hope that others will be inspired to follow in his footsteps—and perhaps avenge his unimaginable fate—the Files of Doctor Qwax have been made available to the author.

This book—our tribute to the Man Who Hunted Aliens— is based on the contents of those files.

Introduction

On a crisp November evening in 1975 (during a period of intense UFO activity), 11 year-old Cyril Courtney was cycling homeward through the gathering dusk. Having just finished his paper-round, Cyril was taking a short cut through the local recreation ground, and wondering if he could persuade his mum to make him a chip butty for supper, when he became aware of a deep, pulsating WHOOM! WHOOM! WHOOM! coming from somewhere overhead.

Even as Cyril glanced up, a dazzling pillar of light struck down from the sky, flooding the penalty-area of a football pitch, about fifty metres away, with an eerie, bluish radiance. And then the thunderstruck boy forgot all about chip butties as he saw the figure which came floating down the column of light.

It resembled a large, fully-equipped police constable. With his hands clasped behind his back, and booted feet slightly apart, he was descending in a purposeful, upright posture, slowly and gently, as if being lowered by an invisible crane.

From behind the park-keeper's hut, where he had taken cover, the trembling Cyril watched the uniformed figure make a perfect, feather-like landing. As suddenly as it had

7

appeared, the mysterious light vanished, and then the 'policeman' set off across the rec at a slow, measured tread, uttering a variety of stern, deep-throated cries, such as "'Allo! 'allo! 'allo! . . . 'Ere, what's your game then, mate?", and, "As hi was proceedin' along the 'igh Street . . .".

Not surprisingly, Cyril Courtney completed the remainder of his journey in record time, and went straight to bed without telling his parents what he had seen. Who would have believed him, anyway? Try telling *your* mum that you have just seen a policeman floating down from the sky, without a parachute, or any other visible means of support, and you'll see what we mean.

If this Handbook had been available in November 1975, poor Cyril might have realised that he had just witnessed the arrival of yet another Alien Being upon the surface of this planet; in this case, by means of an anti-grav beam.

By the time Cyril was persuaded to describe his unnerving experience, several months later, it was, of course, too late. The bogus copper could not be traced. He had become a respectable member of the community, along with countless other aliens which are already in our midst, masquerading as ordinary citizens. Dustmen and doctors, teachers and traffic-wardens. The so-called 'Invasion from Outer-Space' is not just a fantasy, dreamed up by science-fiction writers. IT HAS ALREADY BEGUN!

So what can the man-in-the-street do about it? How are we to combat this insidious threat, when even the Government seems blind to the awful possibility of an extra-terrestrial takeover?

The Handbook could be our last hope. It is designed to establish a vast, undercover army of trained Alien Spotters, dedicated to the task of detecting the enemy, and letting 'him' know that we are on the alert. A.S.S. volunteers will be expected to develop a 'nose' for aliens. They must learn to identify the various alien life-forms, classify their weaknesses, and devise appropriate countermeasures.

But before you accept the challenge, ask yourself the following questions.

Are you ready to embark on a training programme which is three times as dangerous as both World Wars, put together?

Are you certain that you can stay cool, calm and collected, even when confronted by a loathsome, bug-eyed, warty-skinned thing, which looks as if it has just crawled out of a tub of purple slime?

Are you prepared to work in utter secrecy . . . in constant danger of being vapourised, atomised, barbecued by laser-beams, or warped into another dimension?

If your answer to each question is a heroic YES! then you are either half-way round the bend, or just the person we are looking for.

But remember this—HUNTING ALIENS IS A DIRTY BUSINESS! The A.S.S. (Alien-Spotter Service) is under-staffed, unappreciated, and unpaid. Your only reward will be the satisfaction of knowing that, in some, small way, you are helping to Save the Earth.

Is Your Granny an Alien?

The first and most vital quality that the trainee Alien Spotter must develop, is . . . *vigilence*. DON'T TRUST ANYONE!

Even your own grandmother may be possessed by an alien life-form. But before we start on Granny, let's check on YOU first. Are *you* possessed by an alien? Or are you an alien who has changed himself into a reader, so that he can buy this book, and take a sneaky peek at its sensational contents? If you are, we have an unpleasant little surprise for you. Built into page 15 of this book is a Wafer-Thin explosive device, known as the Page 15 Wafer-Thin Explosive Device. It is designed to explode if exposed to the inhuman vibrations of an Alien Presence!

So, if you *are* an alien, the count-down started from the second you opened this book. FIVE . . . FOUR . . . THREE . . . TWO . . . ONE . . . (Please turn to Page 15).

Still with us? Good. This proves you are not an alien, or a human being possessed by one. Now back to Granny. According to the hitherto secret files of Doctor Qwax, many aliens have the power to change their shape to human form (such as the policeman mentioned in the Introduction), while others simply convert themselves into a stream of energy-particles, and take possession of the body of an Earthling.

OOOH! I'VE COME ALL OVER FUNNY!

MUST BE SOMETHING YOU PICKED UP, GRAN!

If your Granny has been invaded in this way, you can soon find out by making a detailed study of her behaviour.

For instance, is your Granny *terrified of thunderstorms*? Does she:

a) keep groaning, 'I think we're in for one.'
b) draw the curtains at the first rumble
c) cover up the mirrors
d) turn off the telly
e) hide under the kitchen table

This is because her alien 'lodger' is frightened that the electrical changes in the atmosphere, created by the storm, will upset his delicate energy-pattern, causing him, or her, to revert to normal shape, and pop out of your Gran at a very awkward moment.

11

Apart from thunderstorms, aliens hate having to possess granny-type Earthlings. They would much rather take over popular people like Kevin Keegan, or Big Daddy, and have a bit of fun. Trapped inside an elderly terrestrial, they tend to become bored and irritable. Is *your* Granny irritable? Is she always grumbling about this and that? And does she *always get her own way*?

As Doctor Qwax points out, the brain-power of many alien beings is superior to that of Earthlings, so your Granny's alien may be forcing her relatives to make a fuss of her by means of *telepathic control*.

To sum up, if your Granny is:

a) terrified of thunderstorms
b) always grumbling about this and that
c) waited on hand, foot and finger by your mum and dad,

she is almost certainly possessed by an Irritable Alien Energy-Form of Superior Intelligence.

You can apply similar alien-spotting tests to virtually any member of the family, simply by watching and listening. Perhaps your Uncle Charlie is always laughing his head off at reports of Flying Saucer sightings. Or perhaps Aunty Doris refers to science-fiction films which feature aliens as 'fanciful balderdash'. Could they be possessed by aliens who are trying to persuade us that the little devils don't exist?

I'LL BET THE HYDROGEN GAS CLOUDS OF THE TRIFID NEBULA LOOK LOVELY AT THIS TIME OF THE YEAR, DAD!

Another useful alien-spotting trick, is to keep chatting to a suspected victim about various parts of the universe. If you hit on the right part, the alien presence may be so overcome with emotion, it will give itself away.

SOB! SOB! STOP IT...YOU'RE MAKING ME HOMESICK!

Detecting aliens which simply change themselves into policemen, traffic-wardens, teachers and other professional people, requires a slightly different approach. When practising at home, the trainee Spotter should confine himself to the tests described above. Obviously, if your grandmother is an alien which has merely changed itself into a granny, it follows that your whole family is composed of aliens. . including yourself.

In which case, you wouldn't be reading this chapter, anyway, because the Page 15 Wafer-Thin Explosive Device would have disposed of you by now (*Hee! Heeeee!*)

EXERCISES

1. Select a member of your family for a full S.A.P. (Suspected Alien Possession) test.

2. If you select your Gran, you will, of course, need a thunderstorm. Trainee Spotters equipped with cassette-recorders should tape a storm as quickly as possible, so that they will always have one handy. (Astute aliens will not be fooled by kids rattling sheets of tin outside the window, and going 'Krak! Brrr-oooomble!')

3. Study as many planets and star-systems as you can, and memorise their characteristics. The poisonous Slith-Weed beds of Flugia, is a good example. You will then be ready to carry out an instant 'homesickness' test.

4. Monitor the relationship between your Mum and your Dad. If your Dad suffers from the condition known as 'Under the Thumb' (characterised by remarks such as 'Yes, Dear. Of course, Dear,' and 'Anything you say, Dear,') this could be further evidence of telepathic control.

5. Keep reading this book until it comes out of your ears.

NOTE:

If any test seems positive, on NO account point at the victim and yell, 'There's an alien inside you, Gran/Mum/Dad/Uncle/Aunty...' The alien just might be a fire-belching Grunf from the Stygian Asteroid-Belt.

Trainee spotters should report their suspicions to the nearest A.S.S. control-centre, before taking any action. (A list of A.S.S. control-centres may be obtained by forwarding a stamped, addressed envelope to Doctor Qwax's secretary, c/o Armada Books.)

THIS WORD SHOULD ONLY BE READ BY ALIENS...

NOW RETURN TO PAGE 10

15

Find the Leaders

Every sabotage squad (or 'Skrutnig') of aliens, is commanded by a Captain (Ptroon), and his Sub-Ptroon—the two leaders being IDENTICAL IN EVERY WAY.

In this display of aliens, the two Ptroons are the ONLY matching pair. Can you pick them out?

This is an important test of observation which could save your life, if and when you encounter a Skrutnig.
(Needless to say, this display was designed by an alien.)

Answer on page 128.

Clues from Constellations

The trainee Spotter should lose no time in building up an Alien Identification Chart, covering various species of alien, their places of origin.

Consider this artist's impression of a creature which was seen peering through the window of a Putney fishmonger, in June, 1949.

OOOPLE GLOOP SNAK *

LONDON

* LEAVE HIM ALONE

Notice the strong resemblance to a Giant Crab?

"So what?" you may scoff. "It might have been a *real* crab which got accidentally exposed to a burst of radiation from a faulty nuclear pile, and turned into a crustacean mutation!"

Oh, yes? Well, take a closer look, clever-clogs. If that's a real crab, what is it doing with a tourist's Guide Map of London?

We would also point out that there are many other alien-sightings on record which feature comparisons with animals. Lions, lizards, bears, and even sea-serpents.

"Hang on a minute," I can hear you exclaim, "All those animals you've just mentioned have got *constellations* named after them!"

17

PRECISELY! Now stand by for a CONSTELLATION QWAX-FAX!

QWAX-FAX

. . .stars were first divided into groups (o Constellations) in Ancient Times, and named after various mythological gods or heroes. Amateur and professional star-gazers still refer to the list of 48 Constellations drawn up by the Greek astronomers, Ptolemy and Hipparchus, over 1,800 years ago. The list featured many animals, and was later extended to include, amongst other things, an air-pump, a telescope, Table Mountain, and a sculptor's workshop.

Even allowing for the fact that the trained Alien-Spotter must be ready for anything, it's a little difficult to imagine an alien shaped like a Sculptor's Workshop.

For the time being, let us put aside the last few objects mentioned in the Qwax-Fax, and concentrate on Hipparchus and Ptolemy.

Ancient Greek astronomers? Not according to Thaddeus Qwax, who points out that Ptolemy is an anagram of 'Yotmelp', which is the home of an alien race, orginating from a planetary system in the constellation CYGNUS (The Swan). One of Yotmelp's two moons is called 'Rhippasuch'. No prizes for guessing that Rhippasuch, spelled another way, reads Hipparchus.

Not surprisingly, Doctor Qwax concluded that H & P weren't astronomers at all, but a pair of artful, super-intelligent aliens who arrived in Ancient Greece round about the year 120 A.D.

At first, they had difficulty with the language; hence the origin of the expression. It's all Greek to me!

But once they had mastered their Latin verbs, the bogus astronomers set about compiling a secret Identification Code, to which all other alien invaders could refer. *The original list of 48 constellations*!

Each constellation marks the sector of the Universe inhabited by a particular alien species, and the *name* of the constellation identifies the Earth-type animal, bird, or sea-creature *which the alien most resembles*.

Thus, the *crab-like* alien would hail from a planetary system in the constellation of CANCER (The Crab); while a creature from URSA MAJOR (The Great Bear), might look

something like this . . .   or this . . .

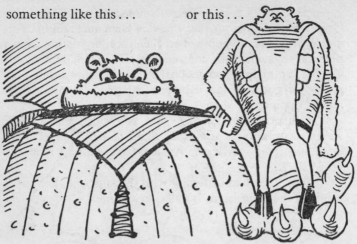

if it came from Ursa MINOR.

Crafty, eh? But thanks to Doctor Qwax' brilliant piece of code-breaking, the Alien-Spotter can now build up his own Alien IDI-CHART, enabling him to determine which part of the Universe an alien life-form comes from, while his knees are still knocking.

Here are a few other examples which you can use as a basis for your chart.

ARIES (The Ram)

CANIS MAJOR
(The Great Dog)

CANIS MINOR (Little Dog)

DRACO
(The Dragon)

SCORPIO
(The Scorpion)

TAURUS
(The Bull)

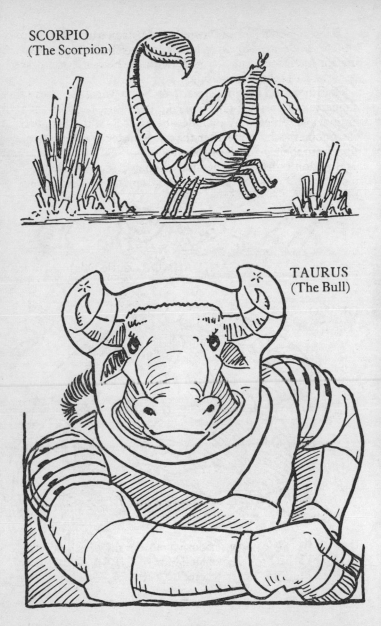

22

There are many other constellations, named after animals, which can be used to extend your Identi-Chart. Try sketching the alien life-forms yourself, with the help of eyewitness reports, and personal sightings.

Confine your list to animals, to begin with. As already suggested, constellations named after objects other than animals were probably included by H & P (and other alien astronomers who came after them), in order to divert attention from their fiendish purpose.

But don't discount the non-animal objects entirely. If more than one Alien-Spotter spots something which looks like this

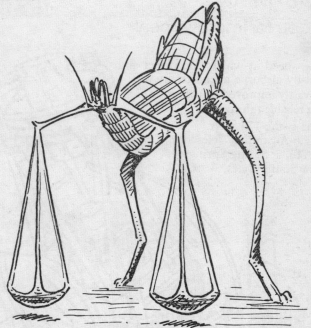

the A.S.S. may have to seriously consider the possibility that SOMEWHERE in the constellation of LIBRA, there exists an alien life-form which resembles a set of scales.

The same applies to Horologium (The Clock), Lyra (The Harp), and Antlia (The Air-Pump).

By now, you should be looking at constellations in a new light—but beware of the most dangerous constellation of all!

If, one dark night, you are confronted by a being which wears a starry sort of sword-belt, at an angle, and goes around waving its arms in the air, it's almost certain that your cover has been broken, and that you are being hunted by a creature from ORION (The Hunter). As he will probably be armed with a Photon Blaster, a Laser-Probe, and a variety of Death-Ray weapons, there is really only one thing you can do . . .

RUUUUUUUN!

Scope for Improvement

The speed at which you detect and classify airborne alien activity will be vastly improved by the acquisition of a reliable telescope.

This is the 154-inch Anglo-Australian Telescope (AAT), at Siding Springs, New South Wales.

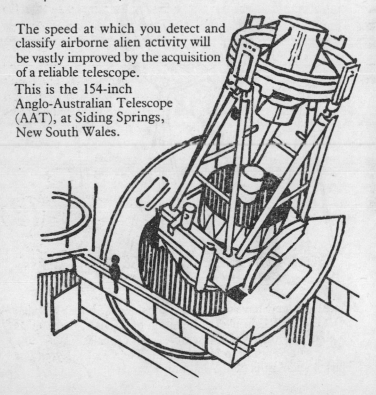

Of course, you won't need one as big as this; not to begin with, anyway. And if you can't afford to buy a telescope, you can build your own quite easily and cheaply. But, first, let's have a quick . . .

TELESCOPIC QWAX-FAX

The Italian scientist and astronomer, Galileo, built the first astronomical telescope in 1609, and trained it on the Moon, Venus, and Jupiter. The first reflecting telescope (using mirrors instead of lenses), was devised by Issac Newton in 1668. The world's largest optical telescope is the 236-inch diameter reflector at Zelenchukskaya, in Russia. Weighing more than 700 tonnes, it is powerful enough to detect the light of a candle from a distance of 15,000 miles.

It is hard to believe that such a powerful telescope hasn't spotted an alien starship by now, so we must assume that it is controlled by aliens disguised as astronomers, or manned by P.H.B.s (Possessed Human Beings).

As this sinister state of affairs probably applies to all those whacking great observatories scattered around the world, the Alien Spotter must rely on the evidence of his own eyes . . . so let's get down to work.

To construct a simple refracting telescope, strong enough to pick out features on the Moon (or the ridges on the forehead of an Altarian Bog-Hopper at five hundred paces), you will need the following materials:

1. Two spectacle lenses; one about 3 inches in diameter (the *Object* glass), and a smaller lens, to act as an *Eye-piece*.
2. Two cardboard tubes; one narrower then the other, so that it can slide in and out of the main tube.
3. Strips of cardboard, and some glue, for fixing the lenses inside the appropriate ends of the tubes.
4. An Assembly Area which cannot be penetrated by P.H.B.s, or A.S.C.s (Alien Shape-Changers).
5. Lots of patience, in case the tubes keep unrolling.

Now follow the various stages, as shown in the illustration.

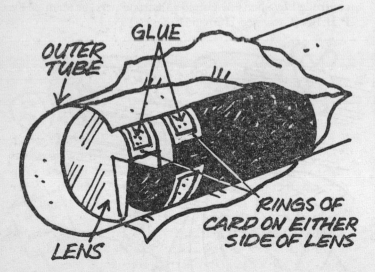

GLUE

OUTER TUBE

LENS

RINGS OF CARD ON EITHER SIDE OF LENS

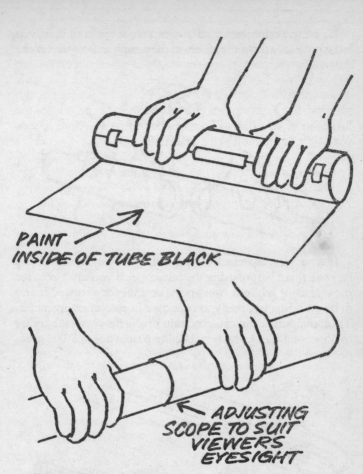

PAINT INSIDE OF TUBE BLACK

ADJUSTING SCOPE TO SUIT VIEWERS EYESIGHT

Fix the Object lens into one end of the larger tube (which should be the same diameter as the lens), and the smaller lens (the Eye-piece) into the outer end of the narrow tube. Connect up the tubes, and adjust the 'focal length' of the telescope to suit your own eyesight, by sliding the narrow tube back and forth, until you obtain the correct focus.

You can improve the efficiency of the telescope by painting the insides of the tubes black, so that all the light from the object you are viewing is concentrated on the lenses.

If, on the other hand, all you can see is a sort of blur, you have probably fixed the lenses to the wrong ends of the tubes.

If you wear spectacles, you will get best results if you remove them before using the telescope. If you can't even see the telescope without your specs, arrange for a trusted friend to be standing by, ready to take over in case of emergencies. This, of course, can cause certain problems if you are trying to observe a UFO which is flashing past at about 5,000 miles per hour.

Should you feel confident enough to have a go at building a more ambitious telescope, such as the 154-inch AAT giant, the use of spectacle lenses, cardboard, and glue is not recommended. Instead, you will require the following bits and pieces:

A Solid Disc Mirror, 154 inches in diameter
36 Support Pads
33 Air Pistons
24 Counterbalanced Mechanical Levers
2 Cassegrain Focal Arrangements
2 Computers for controlling the operation of the 'scope'
1 Central Sky-Baffle
A great big Cage for the observer to sit in
Sundry oil-pad bearings, lengths of tubular steel, more mirrors, photoelectric photometers, bolometers, image scanners, spectographs, etc., etc., etc.

You could be lucky and pick up some of the above items second-hand, or at Reconditioned Telescope auctions. But if you have to buy new parts direct from the manufacturers, don't begrudge the expense. Console yourself with the thought of that glorious moment, when you use your giant telescope for the first time.

Imagine the *thrill* of being able to watch an alien battleship testing its terrifying, flesh-shredding, Gamma-Cannons, as it enters Earth's atmosphere. It's a sight you will remember for the, er . . . rest of your life . . .

NOTE: See APPENDIX A (page 125) for instructions on how to build an Anti-Flesh-Shredding, Gamma-Cannon Shelter.

Alien Identi-Profile No. 1

Species 017/TQ

Classification:	BRASSICOID
Origin:	Ultra-fertile planet in region of Trifid Nebula.
Main Characteristics:	Brassicoids have evolved as plant-forms. They convert sunlight, absorbed through the skin, into energy and protein.

This fully-grown male Brassicoid is seen fertilising a bed of young 'blades', which are not coming on too well. On Earth, Brassicoids tend to shape-change into Gardeners, Grocers, and Park Keepers. The old expression 'born under a gooseberry bush', is probably rooted in Brassicoid folklore.

Sorting out the Stars

Establishing that a particular alien species comes from, say, the constellation Leo, isn't such a feather in your cap if you don't know where Leo is, or what it looks like.

This is Leo (THE LION), best viewed on clear Spring evenings in the Southern skies.

It is easily recognisable here, because the main stars have been joined up by all those handy little lines. Unfortunately, we haven't an artist big enough or tall enough to do a similar job on the whole night sky. But don't despair. All you need to become an expert star-gazer, is a collection of CONSTEL-LATION-SPOTTER CARDS, specially designed by Dr. Qwax (before he disappeared, that is).

TOP-SECRET INSTRUCTIONS FOR THE CONSTRUCTION OF A
CONSTELLATION-SPOTTER CARD.

1. Select a constellation from one of the Star-maps on pages
   36 and 37.
2. Draw an outline of the constellation on a sheet of thin
   paper.
3. Paste the paper on to a piece of strong card (say 8″ x
   4″), and prick a hole through all the stars, like so . . .

4. Write the name of the constellation at the bottom of the
   card.
5 Borrow a torch.
   (If you have just borrowed a torch, *shame on you*! No
   self-respecting Alien Spotter should have to *borrow* such
   a vital piece of equipment).
6. Wait until it gets dark.
7. If it is already dark, go outside.
8. If it's a cloudy night, and you can't see any stars, go back
   inside again, and carry out a quick S.A.P. test on the
   nearest adult.
9. If it's a clear night, follow the example of the A.S. in the
   illustration.

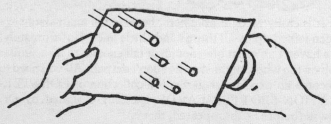

The torchlight will shine through the holes in the card, clearly outlining the constellation you have traced upon it.

10. Keep staring at the sky until you find the constellation which matches the star-group on your card, and note the name of it.

11. Take a week's holiday, and make a Constellation-Spotter Card for every constellation in the sky.

12. Build a handy little box for carrying your C-S cards around in.

TOP-SECRET INSTRUCTIONS FOR BUILDING A
HANDY LITTLE BOX FOR CARRYING YOUR
CONSTELLATION-SPOTTER CARDS AROUND IN.

1. If you are certain that your Dad is not possessed by an alien, ask him if you can borrow his toolbox.

2. If he hasn't got a toolbox . . .

NOTE· We regret that Dr. Qwax disappeared at this point, so you will have to build your own handy little box, or carry the cards around in your pockets.

When studying constellations, it is very important to know exactly where you are. At the end of this section, you will find a list of the constellations which are visible from the British Isles.

If, of course, you are reading this book in Woomera, Australia, the night sky will look somewhat different than it does to an observer standing, say, in the middle of Grimsby Football Ground, so you will have to consult an A.S. Handbook written by someone who lives in Woomera.

On the other hand, if you're absolutely no idea where you are, perhaps it would be best to forget about alien-spotting for the time being, and enrol for a course of Geography lessons.

CONSTELLATIONS WHICH ARE VISIBLE FROM THE BRITISH ISLES.

Latin Name	English Name
ANDROMEDA	Andromeda
AQUARIUS	The Water-Bearer
AQUILA	The Eagle
ARIES	The Ram
AURIGA	The Charioteer
BOOTES	The Herdsman
CAMELOPARDUS	The Giraffe
CANCER	The Crab
CANES VENATICI	The Hunting Dogs
CANIS MAJOR	The Great Dog
CANIS MINOR	The Little Dog
CAPRICORNUS	The Sea-Goat
CASSIOPEIA	*Cassiopeia
CEPHEUS	*Cepheus
CETUS	The Whale
COMA BERENICES	*Berenice's Hair
CORONA BOREALIS	The Northern Crown
CORVUS	The Crow
CRATER	The Cup
CYGNUS	The Swan
DELPHINUS	The Dolphin
DRACO	The Dragon
EQUULEUS	The Little Horse
ERIDANUS	The River
GEMINI	The Twins
HERCULES	Hercules
HYDRA	The Sea-Serpent
LACERTA	The Lizard
LEO	The Lion
LEO MINOR	The Little Lion
LEPUS	The Hare

*Characters from Greek mythology.

LIBRA	The Scales
LYNX	The Lynx
LYRA	The Lyra
MONOCEROS	The Unicorn
OPHIUCHUS	The Serpent-Bearer
ORION	Orion (The Hunter)
PEGASUS	The Flying Horse
PERSEUS	Perseus
PISCES	The Fishes
PISCIS AUSTRALIS	The Southern Fish
SAGITTA	The Arrow
SAGITTARIUS	The Archer
SCORPIO	The Scorpion
SCULPTOR	The Sculptor
SCUTUM SOBIESKII	Sobieski's Shield
SERPENS	The Serpent
SEXTANS	The Sextant
TAURUS	The Bull
TRIANGULUM	The Triangle
URSA MAJOR	The Great Bear
URSA MINOR	The Little Bear
VIRGO	The Virgin
VULPECULA et ANSERIS	The Fox and Goose.

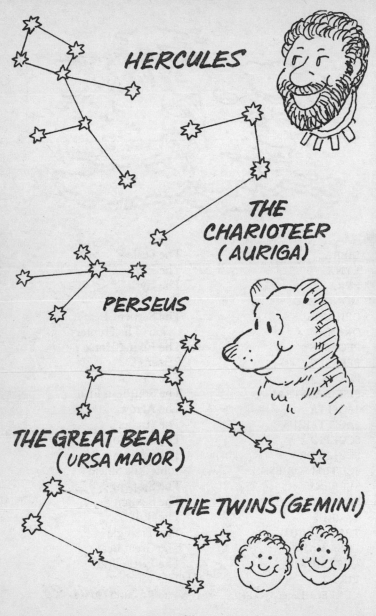

HERCULES

THE CHARIOTEER (AURIGA)

PERSEUS

THE GREAT BEAR (URSA MAJOR)

THE TWINS (GEMINI)

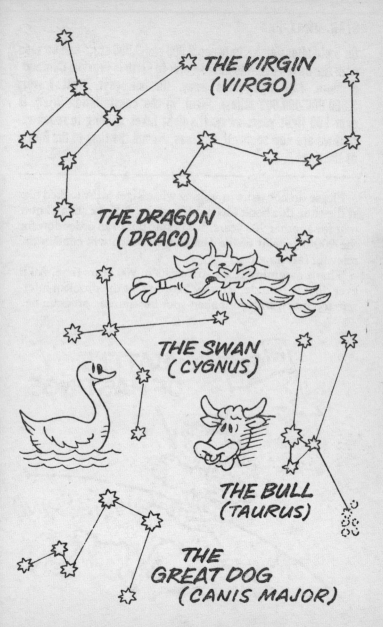

THE VIRGIN
(VIRGO)

THE DRAGON
(DRACO)

THE SWAN
(CYGNUS)

THE BULL
(TAURUS)

THE
GREAT DOG
(CANIS MAJOR)

STAR QWAX-FAX

On a cloudless night, between 2,000 and 3,000 stars can be seen with the naked eye. The nearest star to Earth is Proxima Centauri, a mere 4.27 light-years away. (In one year, light travels 5,880,000,000,000 miles). Rigel, in the constellation Orion, is over 900 light-years away. It's light takes so long to reach us, that we are now seeing it as it was, around the time of the Battle of Hastings.

Please do not write in, asking what Rigel *really* looked like at the time this book was published, because we shan't know that for another 900 years. It's best to put in an order now for the 900th reprint of the Handbook, which will contain the relevant information.

That's assuming Rigel still exists in 900 years time. All it ever does is twinkle, anyway, so don't let the problem interfere too much with your alien-spotting training programme.

Trace the Face

Here is the star-map of a constellation discovered by Doctor Qwax, just before he disappeared. As yet un-named, the constellation is believed to be inhabited by a particularly gruesome alien species, which grunts a lot.

Join up the numbered stars, to discover why the Doctor describes these creatures as 'PORCUPODS'.

A Spotter's-Eye View of the World's Greatest Mysteries

There's nothing like a good mystery, is there? Throughout recorded history, men have sought for the answers to a wide variety of weird and wonderful occurrences. On land and sea, and in the air, strange things have happened (and are still happening) which continue to baffle the experts. At least, that is what they call themselves. If these highly-paid investigators had access to the knowledge and experience of the astute Alien Spotter, they wouldn't look so baffled! The World's Greatest Mysteries (heh! heh!) would begin to yield up their secrets.

Take the 'mystery' of the Marie Celeste, for instance. This American brigantine was found adrift in mid-Atlantic, in November, 1872, a month after sailing from New York. The ship was in full sail, and in perfect order—yet there was not a soul on board!

What had happened to the crew? Why had they abandoned the vessel in the middle of a meal, without even pausing to lower a life-boat?

Pirates?

The sudden appearance of a sea-monster, causing the terrified matelots to jump overboard? Perhaps.

But as the veteran Spotter well knows, even Aliens can make mistakes . . .

41

As our reconstruction of the disaster suggests, someone was a bit heavy-handed with the levitation-beam.

But aliens are in the habit of *dropping* things, as well, which may account for the curious phenomenon know as SHOWERS OF FROGS AND TOADS.

According to reliable sources, including *The Times*, a torrent of toads deluged the French village of Brignoles, in 1973. In the same year, a rain of frogs stopped play on an American golf-course, in the middle of a thunderstorm. 'Whirlwinds!' claimed the experts. Freak weather conditions which scooped up our amphibian friends, and deposited them in another place.

But just think about it for a moment. If aliens are in the habit of sucking up sailors for study and analysis, why not frogs . . . or toads?

Which disposes of yet another 'mystery'.

It is perhaps reassuring to know that some aliens are 'only human', as it were. But another famous mystery—the celebrated case of the Devil's Hoofprints—was probably the result of equipment malfunction.

The strange tracks, or 'hoofprints', appeared during a night in February, 1855, following a heavy fall of snow in South Devon. Horrified Devonians woke up to discover that an unknown 'creature', endowed with supernatural powers had gone on a walk-about through several towns; sauntering casually over houses, straight up sheer walls, and clean through haystacks without disturbing a single strand of hay . . .

The usual crop of explanations included otters, badgers, rats, and even the trailing-rope of a balloon.

But the A.S.S. knows of at least one race of lazy aliens who prefer to send down Robot Search-Probes, rather than investigate the terrain in person. And suppose, as we have already suggested, that one of these probes went out of control, on a winter's night in South Devon, 1855 . . .

There seems little doubt that alien activity is at the root of our next 'mystery', which concerns the intriguing theory of the Hollow Earth.

Ancient myths and legends would have us believe that the centre of the Earth contains vast, subterranean worlds, populated by a variety of trolls, gnomes, kobbolds, and sundry other Little Folk.

But an American UFO logist may be closer to the truth. He claims that there is an enormous hole at the North Pole, a gigantic fault in the Earth's crust, through which alien ships have been sneaking for centuries.

At this very moment, they may be preparing to invade us from WITHIN!

How else can you explain the increase in the popularity of the 'sport' of pot-holing? Do people *really* get any pleasure out of donning helmets and heavy packs, and burrowing down into the depths of the earth like demented moles?

Of course they don't! A.S.S. investigations suggest that the pot-holers are themselves cleverly-disguised aliens, delivering mail, messages and little comforts to their comrades down below.

And so we come to the 'mystery' of Stonehenge. Built in several stages from 2900 B.C. to 1400 B.C., this rather untidy collection of standing stones on Salisbury Plain, has been variously described as a place of worship; a sort of ancient disco, where horrible sacrifices took place, and even a Neolithic computer. (Not a bad effort, that).

But if we examine this diagram of Stonehenge as it must have appeared, thousands of years B.F.T. (Before Foreign Tourists)...

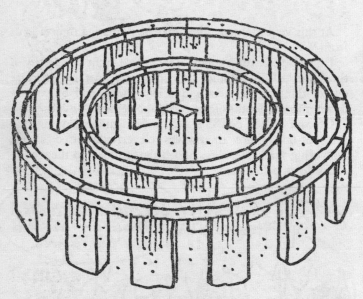

Doesn't it look just a little like a collection of giant skittles, neatly-arranged for the start of a game?

As an experienced Spotter will tell you, aliens come in all shapes and sizes. The savage Merakians of Ursa Major, for example, reach heights of twenty metres and more, when fully-grown. And when you are stationed on a strange planet, thousands of light-years from home, you've got to find *some* way of amusing yourself haven't you?

It is little wonder that Stonehenge is in such a delapidated state!

Need we go on? Take almost any 'Great Mystery' at random, add a dash of Alien Influence, and the pieces will begin to fall into place (or out of place, as in the case of Stonehenge). Have a shot at solving a few mysteries yourself, and you will see how easy it is.

Start with the Loch Ness Monster, if you like. Could 'Nessie' be a type of alien submarine, which pops up now and then to have a look at *us* . . . looking at *it*?

Is the Abominable Snowman nothing more than a big, hairy probe, which has been plodding around the Himalayas ever since its homing-circuits failed?

Perhaps there are unsolved mysteries in your own locality; such as the legendary Black Dog, or 'Old Shuck', which has been scaring the daylights out of people for hundreds of years, all over the British Isles.

Now if we consider the possibility that many aliens have brought their pets with them, for company, and that some of these alien animals have escaped, or gone walkies without their owners . . .

The A.S.S. strikes again.

Spotter's Knock

No, it isn't a disease which afflicts Alien Spotters. We are talking about the 'Secret Knock' which should be used by a Spotter when calling upon a fellow Spotter, who needs to be reassured that there isn't a Ligurian Zlit from Jelda 4, waiting hungrily on the doorstep.

This month's Knock, based on a sonic rhythm perfected by Dr. Qwax, is outlined below. It should be delivered with the knocking arm slightly bent, and the hand formed into a fist.

SECRET KNOCK (© Dr. T. QWAX)

Knock! Knock! Knock! ... Knock! Knock ! ... Knockety-Knock! Knock! ... Knock-Knockety! ... KNOCK! Knock! Knock! ... Scrape! Tap! Knock! ... Knock! Knock! Knock! ... Tap! Knockety-KNOCK!

(Change from right hand to left hand, or vice versa. Continue knocking, a little more insistently.)

Thak! Thak! ... Thak! Thak! Thak! ... Thakkety-Thak-Thak! THONNK! ... Thak! Rap! ... Rappety-Rap-Rap! ... BLAM! ... Thak! Thonk! ... Rattle! Rattle! .. CRAAAASH!

(If, at this point, there is still no answer, apply protective bandages to finger-joints. Continue knocking with maximum urgency.)

Thunk! ... Thunk! Thunk! ... Thunk! Thunk! Thunkety-Thunk! ... Thwud-Thunk! ... Thud! BLAAAAM! ... KICK! KRUUNCH! BDAAAAAAAM! SPLINTER!

On completion of Secret Knock, wait in utter silence for three minutes. If your colleague fails to answer the door within that time, he is either:

1. already liquidated
2. cleaning his football boots in the garage
3. totally absorbed in his copy of the Handbook
4. using last month's Secret Knock, and therefore ignoring you because he suspects a trick
5. at your house, knocking on *your* door

Your fellow Spotter's lack of response may also be due to the fact that your Secret Knock contains an error. For example, you may have *Thunked*! when you should have *Thakkety-Thakked*! So check back carefully through the sequence of knocks before taking any further action.

Do NOT start shouting 'Aww, come on Brian/Gavin/Ian/Trevor/Dennis/Karen/Greavesey . . .' etc. etc.! 'Stop messing about and open the door!' Such a display of impatience and bad temper will not help to Save the Earth.

For Spotters with tender finger-joints, Reinforced Secret Knock Gloves may be obtained from any A.S.S. Control Centre at our special discount price of £199.50. Applications should be accompanied by your A.S.S. Number, and a 40p postal-order to cover postage.

Spotter in a Spot

This potholing Alien Spotter has been spotted spying on a colony of subterranean Stygians—and now they're after him!

Unfortunately, he has lost his route map in the confusion, and only one of those tunnel-mouths leads back to the surface. Can you help him to choose the right one, so that he can give the Stygians the slip, and report his discovery to the A.S.S.?

Answer on page 128.

2000 A.D.

Fortunately, not all the aliens which have visited our fair planet are a danger to us. We know of at least one who bitterly resents the damage which subversive and hostile alien species are causing to his reputation.

His name is THARG THE MIGHTY.

He is also known (or so he informed Dr. Qwax in a recent interview), as Lord of the Dimensions, and Master of the Time Lanes; and he hails from a planet which orbits Betelgeuse. Which is the cue for yet another, highly-informative

---

QWAX-FAX

Betelgeuse is a red 'supergiant' star which forms the left 'shoulder' of the constellation Orion (The Hunter). It is best viewed on clear winter evenings in the South, and is easily visible with the naked eye. Betelgeuse is the 10th brightest of the known stars (excluding our own Sun, of course), and is over 600 light-years from Earth. It is so big that if Betelgeuse was placed at the centre of the Solar System, its outer rim would extend beyond the orbit of the Earth around the Sun.

With the exception of Dr. Qwax, no one can say for certain just how or when Tharg first appeared on Earth; but the Mighty One's chief claim to fame is that he produces a comic called 2000 A.D., from a spaceship in London. The ship is disguised as a giant office tower, and is staffed entirely by robots which write and illustrate 2000 A.D. under Tharg's strict supervision.

Tharg's mortal enemies are the loathsome Dictators of Zrag, one of the deadliest alien life-forms to have visited this planet. The Dictators detest Tharg's benevolent attitude towards humans, and the way he encourages readers of 2000

A.D. to submit reports of alien sightings. Some of the sketches of alien life-forms which accompanied these reports are reproduced below.

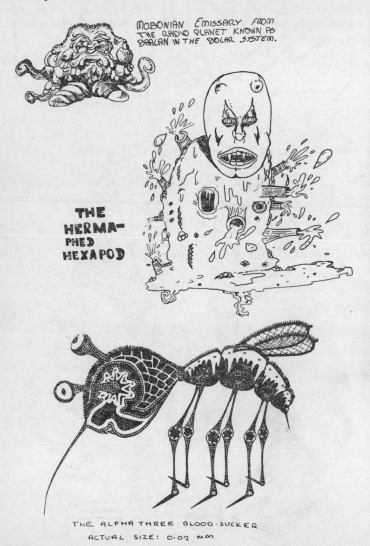

MOBONIAN EMISSARY FROM THE RADIO PLANET KNOWN AS BAALAN IN THE BOLAR SYSTEM.

THE HERMA- PHED HEXAPOD

THE ALPHA THREE BLOOD-SUCKER
ACTUAL SIZE: 0.02 MM

Dr. Qwax has always recommended that all Spotters should carry a copy of 2000 A.D., wherever they go, for the purpose of *mutual identification*. The comic should be kept out of sight, of course, and only displayed when you are absolutely certain that you are in the presence of another Spotter.

And now, by kind permission of the Mighty One, we are proud to present a selection of Betelgeusian Phrases.

BORAG THUNGG	Galactic Greetings!
SPLUNDIG VUR THRIGG	Farewell!
ZARJAZ	Fantastic
GHAFFLEBETTE	Out of This World
KRILL THRO THARGO	Honoured by Tharg. (Awarded to Spotters who have excelled themselves in the field).
QUAEQUAM BLAG	Stone Me! My Goodness! Strewth!
FLORIX GRABUNDAE	Many Thanks
FROGNUM GRUELIS	April Fool!

55

Alien Identi-Profile No. 2

Species 024/TQ

Classification:	JELDIAN MONITOR
Origin:	Admin planet of the Fifth Magellanic Empire.
Main Characteristics:	Monitors are semi-organic, and used solely in a Police/Security role. Genetic engineering has given them a third, infra-red eye, to ensure maximum efficiency during night-patrols.

Snooty Traffic-Wardens, hyper-stern Headmasters, and Overbearing Aunties are probably possessed by Jeldian Monitors. Also bad-tempered Police Constables who favour the catch-phrase 'I've got me eye on you, my lad!'

Funny People These Earthlings

The aliens think so, anyway. Examination of letters and reports, intercepted by the A.S.S., reveal that quite ordinary Earthly pursuits take on an entirely new meaning when viewed through alien eyes.

Study the following extracts from alien correspondence, and then see if you can identify the six objects, or events, which they are describing. (*The answers are on page 128.*)

1. '... these containers cannot be very valuable, because the Earthlings are extremely careless with them. They put them outside their houses at night, and in the morning other Earthlings—accompanied by large, cumbersome vehicles—roam the streets, and steal the material from the containers, to the accompaniment of a great deal of banging and shouting...'

2. '... the players spent most of their time singing, and chanting, and indulging in pitched battles. Only twenty-three spectators, one of whom was armed with a whistle, watched the display from a grassed area at the centre of the arena...'

3. '... in exasperation at not receiving a reply to my questions, I detached the creature's long, flexible appendage from its stomach-vent. It promptly gave off a loud, whirring noise, and began to flash its eyes at me...'

4. '... at one point, several giant parrots rushed up ladders, and attacked coloured balloons filled with water, before nose-diving into large vats of liquid. The ritual was accompanied by screams of laughter from the Earthling in charge...'

5. '... Great News! I have managed to infiltrate an A.S.S. meeting! Both males and females were present, and they were addressed from a platform by a single Earthling, who called out a succession of numbers. It was undoubtedly a form of code, which I am still trying to decipher...'

How to make a Big Impression and Influence Aliens

Observing alien activity from a safe distance is all very well, but what would you do if you were actually *confronted* by an Extra-terrestrial Being? (A Close Encounter of the Third or Fourth Kind.) Or, worse still, a whole skrutnig of them?

Spotters who are equipped with bicycles, or lightning reflexes, may stand an outside chance of escaping with nothing more serious than a few laser-burns or energy-bolt blisters. But if you are alone, on foot, and completely surrounded, all you can really do (apart from fainting, and screaming for help), is to try and *bluff* your way out: by staging such a spectacular display of apparent SUPER-POWER, that the aliens will fall back in awe and terror, and allow you to pass on your way unscathed.

Although we don't *guarantee* success, here are a few little tricks which usually help to create a Big Impression.

THE INCREDIBLE BOUNCING COMIC

This is where your copy of 2000 A.D. will come in handy. (If you have forgotten to bring it, you don't deserve to survive anyway.)

You should have prepared the comic *before* setting out on your mission, by gluing a small, rubber-composition Super-ball to the back of Tharg's masterpiece.

Informing the aliens that you have given the comic the power to defy gravity, throw it smartly to the ground. Imagine the stunned expression on their loathsome faces, when your copy of 2000 A.D. 'levitates' smartly back into your hand!

The only problem with this trick, is that the aliens may challenge you to do it with your whole body. A.S.S. scientists are, at this precise moment, working overtime to perfect a pair of Anti-Gravity Boots, which will be available in various sizes. Unfortunately, they are encountering a few problems with the G.I.C. (Grav-Input Control), which brings the boots down again.

In the meantime, you will have to rely on your comic, and hope for the best.

THE AMAZING EDIBLE CANDLE

While your comic is still bouncing, produce what appears to be a lighted candle, and *start eating it!*

Of course, it isn't a candle at all. It's really a cylindrical piece of banana (or cucumber), which has been peeled, and cut into shape, like so . . .

BRAZIL
NUT
↙ WICK

Into one end of the 'candle', insert a sliver of brazil nut, which acts as a wick (you can actually light it, honest!). Don't overdo things by attempting to carve out a *holder* for your candle. The aliens may get fed up waiting, and liquidate you. Apart from that, you will need several pounds of bananas, or cucumbers, and the local grocer's shop may have closed.

THE POTATO TRAP

On *no* account attempt any tricks involving a potato. Earthlings who wash, scrape, chop and boil potatoes before mashing them are greeted with contemptuous laughter by certain species of aliens.

On the other hand, if you can produce a packet of the *instant mash* variety, it will instantly command their respect.

If there is a wall nearby, instruct one of the aliens to stand against it, so that his arm is pressing against the wall, from his shoulder to his finger-tips (or his webbed talons, if he's a Denebian Amphibanoid). Make him stand like that for a full minute, pressing against the wall as hard as he can.

Then, after telling him to stand away from the wall, wave your hands like a magician and call out, in your best, dramatic voice, 'Arm .. I COMMAND you to levitate!'

To the alien's astonishment, the arm will promptly obey, rising slowly to shoulder height without any effort on the part of its owner!

Don't ask us how, but this really works. If your victim has more than one arm, the effect will be even more impressive.

This is easily the most impressive demonstration of super-power in the Spotter's repertoire, and also the trickiest—because you will need a Total Eclipse of the Sun to bring it off.

It won't work at night, so you must make sure that you are captured in broad daylight, when the Sun is shining from a cloudless sky.

You have already checked that the moon is about to pass between the Sun and the Earth, so that the three celestial bodies are in direct line. Wait until the eclipse is beginning, then turn to the aliens with as much disdain as you can muster, and inform them that, as a final warning that you are not to be tampered with, you have decided to *steal the Sun out of the sky*!

Lo and behold, as the Moon draws completely over the Sun, and its shadow touches the Earth, the sky will darken, and stars become visible. Uttering cries of terror, the aliens will then prostrate themselves at your feet, groaning and wailing, and begging you to put the Sun back.

A word of caution. All aliens, by their very nature, are seasoned space-travellers, so they may know all about solar eclipses.

It should also be noted that the next total eclipse of the Sun which is visible from Britain, will not take place until 11th August, 1999, so you should arrange to be captured on that date if you wish to attempt this particular trick.

Partial eclipses, visible from Britain, will occur on 15th December 1982, 30th May 1984, 10th May 1994, and 12th October 1996, but these are not nearly so effective for the purposes of impressing aliens.

If, after all this, you have failed to convince them that they are dealing with a superior being, you could try waving a replica of the Handbook at them. The very sight of it may make them fly into such a rage, their atomic balance will be momentarily shattered. You will then be able to run for your life while the aliens are collecting themselves.

* On no account use a *genuine* copy of the Handbook.
  See chapter entitled AAARTHA!'.

Alien Identi-Profile No. 3

Species 033/RB (Discovered by Roger Bicknell of Tattenhall, Cheshire).

Classification:	RIGELLIAN PIRATE
Origin:	Unknown
Main Characteristics:	Reptilian. Preys on supply-ships ferrying cargo to the mining communities of the Thravian Asteroid fields, at the rim of Rigel's ecosphere.

Utterly villainous and treacherous, R-Pirates are outlawed by most other alien races. The individual exposed by Roger Bicknell was nicking bikes from a comprehensive school, under the guise of a kindly lollipop lady.

Place the Porcupods

This Spotter has stumbled on an abandoned Porcupod ship . . . or *is* it abandoned? If you look closely at the picture, you will find that these shape-changing aliens have merged themselves with the instrumentation.

Locate as many Porcupods as you can, before checking your total against the correct answer, on Page 128.

Alien Breakers

Aliens have been 'breaking' into various channels on Citizens' Band Radio, and using their own slang expressions, and call-signs, to pass vital messages.

Examples of their gruesome gobbledygook are listed below. Spotters with access to C.B.R. equipment may be able to add to the list.

ATOM CRACKER	Alien energy-biscuit
ACE INVADER	Alien who has visited the Earth many times
ANCIENT BRITON	English Astronaut
BIG SUCKER	Black Hole
BOOMERANG BUS	Space Shuttle
BUMPER BUNDLE	The Universe
BUSYBODY	Possessed Human Being on Specific Mission
CHEMISTRY SET	Space Lab
CHOCOLATE SOLDIER	Mars
CHOCOLATE WHIRL	Spiral Galaxy
DISNEYLAND	Pluto
DOUBLE TOP	Two-Headed Alien
FAR OUT	Uranus
FARTHER OUT	Neptune
FLYIN' LION	Constellation Leo
FLY PAST	Dead Fly
GOOD BODY	Human Being suitable for Possession
GREAT BEAR IN THE AIR	Ursa Major
GROUND STAFF	Alien established on Earth
GROUNDNUT	Homesick and mentally-unstable Alien
GROUP	Planetary System
HAPPY HUNTING GROUNDS	Solar system
HIGH-SPEED GAS	Comet
HOME-FROM-HOME	Earth

HOOPLA CHAMPION	Saturn
HOT ROCK	Meteor
HOT ROCKLING	Meteorite
JUPITER	Jupiter
KEELED-OVER-KEEGAN	Collapsed Star
LITTLE BEAR IN THE AIR	Ursa Minor
MEALS ON WHEELS	Earth Motorists
MICKY MOUSE MODULATION	Citizens Band Radio
MOLE	Subterranean Alien
NIGHT-LIGHT	The Moon
ODD BODY	Earthling unsuitable for possession
ONE-HUNDRED-AND-EIGHTY!	Mission achieving maximum success
PAIN-IN-THE-NECK	Star-gazing Spotter
PAPER STAR	The Sun
POSITION FILLED	Possessed Earthling
ROCK FESTIVAL	Asteroid Belt
ROUNDABOUT	Satellite
ROYAL COMMAND PERFORMANCE	Galaxy (Vast array of stars)
SHAKIN' STEVENS	Vibrating Star
SILVER BALL	Mercury
SKY-JACK	Theft of any Earth space-vehicle by Aliens
SKY-JOKE	Weather Satellite
SPOILSPORT	Alien Spotter
SUPER-GROUP	Constellation
SQUATTER	Alien who specialises in Possession
USED NEWSPAPER	Red Sun
UGLY DUCK	Constellation Cygnus (The Swan)
WALKIES	Space Walk (Especially aliens originating from a planet orbiting Sirius, the 'Dog' star)

Careless Creatures

The UFO (Unidentified Flying Object) which appeared over Budleigh Salterton in April, 1969, attracted quite a crowd, which included several ALIEN SHAPE CHANGERS. Carried away by the excitement, each alien relaxed his 'Molecular Aura' to such an extent, that part of his body reverted to normal shape. Can you spot the six, gruesome give-aways? (You will find the answers on page 128.)

This is a reproduction of a photograph taken by Dr. Qwax.

Alien Identi-Profile No. 4

Species 042/TQ

Classification: Stygian Vlad

Origin: Dark side of moon orbiting Deneb Algedi 7, in Capricornus.

Main Characteristics: Vlad's are carbon dioxide-breathing carnivores. Armed with blow-pipes, through which they fire poisoned teeth, they spend their lives in perpetual darkness, hunting the elusive Korp'ussyls on which they feed.

Vlads arrive on Earth in pressurised capsules, and undergo a long acclimatisation period underground. The likely origin of the Dracula legend, they masquerade as Grave Diggers, and Mortuary Attendents, and slot easily into the 'shock-horror' category of pop-group.

The Peterborough Probe

The vast majority of Earthlings are, of course, utterly unaware that our society is riddled with hostile aliens, so you may not be surprised to learn that certain, misguided scientists are going to great lengths to *establish contact* with them!

Consider this extract from the Files of Doctor Qwax:

QWAX-FAX—Messenger to the Stars

Space-probe Pioneer 10 was launched from Earth in 1972 for the purpose of studying the planets Jupiter and Saturn. It was followed by Pioneer 11 in 1973. Fixed to each probe is an engraved metal plaque showing the figures of a man and a woman, a diagram of the Solar System, and the location of the Earth in relation to nearby 'pulsar' stars*.

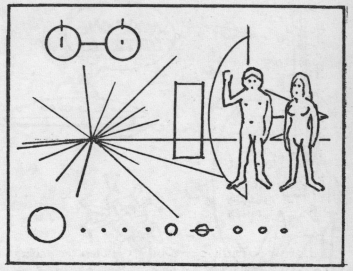

* For the benefit of Spotters who like to collect Amazing Facts, a Pulsar (according to Earth astronomers) is a dense, collapsed star, which emits rapid pulses of radio-waves. That is what they would have us believe, anyway.

Voyager Probes 1 and 2, launched in 1977, are much more ambitious. Each one contains a long-playing record, with 116 colour pictures of Earth, its life, and technology, electronically 'encoded' into its grooves. There are also a variety of typical Earth noises, greetings in various languages, followed by a selection of the Earth's Greatest Hits, ranging from Bach to Chuck Berry. Lovers of folk-music are catered for with Aborigine songs, and a Navajo Indian chant.

Once the four probes have completed their planned missions, they will be allowed to drift out of the Solar System, and carry their cosmic 'greeting cards' on and on through inter-stellar space, until, it is hoped, they are intercepted by an intelligent life-form.

With so many alien ships plying the spaceways around our planet, it is almost certain that the interception has already taken place. And we who know our aliens can just imagine the scene . . .

Perhaps it was the Pioneer and Voyager missions which inspired a treacherous thought in the brain of an alien propaganda expert. If these stupid Earthlings are so keen to contact us, why don't *we* send a messenger probe to *them*?

So they did.

Launched by a mother-ship from somewhere outside the Solar System, the probe survived the descent through the Earth's atmosphere, and landed in a field of sugar beet on the outskirts of Peterborough, shortly before this book was published. Had the probe been found by unsuspecting Earthlings, the consequences could have been disastrous, for it contained 'greeting cards' which, to the untrained eye, conveyed the impression that the senders were the nicest, and friendliest creatures that you could ever wish to meet.

Like the Pioneer probes, the alien vehicle bore a metal plate, inscribed with various symbols. The details of the plaque, together with a rough translation of the alien text, are reproduced below.

Have some fun, indeed! Fortunately for the Earth, this cosmic confidence trick was tracked by one of Doctor Qwax' satellites, located by vigilant Spotters, and spirited away by the A.S.S., seconds before a puzzled farm-worker arrived on the scene.

But the Peterborough Probe should not be dismissed as an alien plot that failed (if we forget the twisted knee sustained by the farm-worker when he fell into the hole which had been made by the probe), for the contents have revealed some useful insights into Alien Culture. Their taste in music, for example. The kind of jokes that make them laugh.

The following list of alien funnies were taken from a video-disc found inside the probe.

Knock! Knock!
Who's there?
Jupiter!
Jupiter who?
Jupiter Rigellian rock-snake in my bed?

Knock! Knock!
Who's there?
Eclipse!
Eclipse who?
Eclipse you round the ear for being cheeky, our Dad does!

Ugh! You're right. Jokes like that are best confined to Christmas crackers. But they get better as we go along.

What do space-travellers use to keep their trousers up?
Asteroid belts.

Why has a Pavonian Dung-Stalker got such long legs?
Because it can't stand the smell of its feet.

What do you get if you cross a UFO with a baby?
An Unidentified Crying Object.

What do you get if you cross a UFO with a sausage?
An Unidentified Frying Object.

Construct a sentence which includes the word 'alienate'.
Our Mum threw out some mouldy bread pudding for the birds, but an alien ate it.

A species of pygmy alien on Deneb 4 rushed into a doctor's surgery and shouted, 'Doctor, you promised that those pills you gave me would make me tall, but nothing's happened yet!'

'Sorry,' said the doctor, 'you'll just have to be a little patient.'

The musical content of the Peterborough Probe was quite surprising. The author has listened to some of the tracks, and arranged the best of them into an Extraterrestrial Top Ten.

1. METEORIC ROCK .... Falling Stones
2. JUST WARPING IN THE RAIN .... Time Machine
3. YOU'LL NEVER SPACE-WALK ALONE ..... Astronuts
4. ONE LOVELY BACK EYE .... Cyclops
5. BY THE LIGHT
   OF THE SILVERY EARTH .... Luna-Beats
6. PUT YOUR HEADS ON MY SHOULDER .... Two Faces
7. THE GRYMES*
   THEY ARE A-CHANGING .... Metamorphs
8. AROUND THE WORLD
   IN 80 SECONDS .... Super-Satellite
9. SULPHUR-JELLY FIELDS .... Beatlegeuse
10. BLACK HOLE BOOGIE .... Star Attraction

And now for some Alien Poetry!

Hey, Zirra! Zirra!
The Vlot and the Jirra
The Nunge jumped over the Earth.
The little Mij laughed to see such fun,
And the Garj ran away with Zyrth!

Where have we heard *that* before? There is also something vaguely familiar about the item which follows the nursery rhyme. Entitled BEAUTY AND THE GROYLK it appears to be an alien variation on a well-known fairy tale.

---

* Shape-Changers from very dense planet. Grymes specialise in Heavy Metal Rock musicians.

77

79

You may agree that this enchanting little tale bears a strong resemblance the style of Bartholomew Wedgewood Jimson, the world-famous writer of children's stories, who took off in a hot-air balloon from a cricket pitch in Runcorn, in 1897, and was never seen again.

Was he, in fact, an alien? Recalled to his home planet to pave the way for such projects as the Peterborough Probe?

If so, then we must face up to the grim possibility that many of our best-loved nursery rhymes and fables were probably penned by alien authors.

And if you are wondering what they hope to gain by invading the gentle world of children's literature, just think about it. Earthlings who have been brought up on a literary diet of witches, hobgoblins and talking animals are much more likely to accept a Thing from Outer Space as just another lovable 'bogieman'. A bit scary, but lovable with it.

A range of Video-Games, found inside the probe, is an obvious attempt to encourage us to believe this. Such offerings as 'Festival of the Planets', 'Friendly Invaders', and 'Fun in Space', all portray the enemy as a jolly decent sort. But even aliens can make mistakes. One of the vid-game cartridges seems to have been stowed aboard the probe in error, because it finally exposes this 'warm-hearted' salute from the stars as nothing but an invitation to global disaster.

The illustration below features a clip from the game, which is called 'Hunt the Earthling'.

Speaks for itself, doesn't it? Now we know what games aliens *really* play when they are at home.

And the moral of this chapter is... if you should come across an extraterrestrial probe, stuck in a sugar beet field just outside Peterborough—or anywhere else, for that matter—DON'T BELIEVE A WORD OF IT!

A Code that Gets Results

The A.S.S. has created a simple, but ingenious code which Spotters should use for sending messages, and transmitting reports. Take a look at this.

ARSENAL	1	LIVERPOOL	9
IPSWICH	5	EVERTON	1
COVENTRY	5	BRIGHTON	0
WOLVES	6	MIDDLESBRO'	2
GRIMSBY	1	CHARLTON	2
STOKE	2	TOTTENHAM	5
SUNDERLAND	4	MAN CITY	0

Decoded, this message reads 'ALIEN SIGHTED'.

The key to the code is *the number of goals scored by each team*; because this is the figure which determines the *letter* that each football club supplies to the completed message.

For instance, the scoreline 'Arsenal 1' gives you the letter A—the *first* letter in the word 'Arsenal'. 'Liverpool 9' is decoded as 'L'—the *ninth* letter in the word 'Liverpool'*. 'Ipswich 5' becomes 'I', and so on.

Where '0' appears after a team, this indicates the completion of a word—a gap between two words. Write down each letter as it is decoded, starting from the top of the column of results, and working from left to right, as you move down.

BAH! ITS ONLY A LIST OF FOOTBALL RESULTS!

HOW MANY SCORE DRAWS?

---

* If you prefer Arsenal to win, the scoreline ARSENAL 6, LIVERPOOL 1, would also give you the letters A and L.

You can vary the code by arranging with your fellow-spotters that, for a specified period, the letter-count will be, say, *one less* than the number of goals scored; so that 'BOLTON 4' indicates the letter 'L' instead of 'T'.

The great strength of our football code lies in its sheer simplicity. Even if a message fell into the hands of the enemy, it is doubtful if they would even *recognise* it as a coded message.

But make sure that your results are reasonably realistic. Remember that many aliens are masquerading as professional footballers, and scorelines such as 'MANCHESTER UNITED 1, TUTTS CLUMP RESERVES 7' may arouse their suspicions. Even aliens who cannot stand soccer must be aware that Manchester United and Tutts Clump Reserves play in different leagues.

Now see if you can decode the following list of results. Start with the column on the left—working from left to right.

BIRMINGHAM	4	COVENTRY	8
EVERTON	0	SUNDERLAND	2
ARSENAL	5	IPSWICH	6
LIVERPOOL	1	SWANSEA	6
SPURS	0	BRIGHTON	5
BARNSLEY	2	GRIMSBY	5
BOLTON	0	WREXHAM	1
ORIENT	4	DERBY	4
BLACKBURN	1	CHELSEA	3
WATFORD	7	CARDIFF	0
FULHAM	1	PRESTON	3
NEWPORT	2	PETERBORO	3

You will find the decoded message on page 128.

NOTE: The above results are entirely imaginary, and do not represent the author's opinion of the ability of any Association Football club, alive or dead.

AAARTHA!

Memorise the above word until you know it was well as your own name—because it describes the state of battle-readiness that the trainee Spotter should aim for . . . AAARTHA!

Always Armed and Ready to Hunt Aliens.

And always *means* always. Experienced Spotters never go anywhere without the alien-hunting devices already described in this book, plus one or two others which we shall discuss in this chapter.

Be prepared . . . be vigilant . . . be AAARTHA!

The most important piece of equipment in the Spotter's armoury is, of course, his copy of the Handbook. *But don't forget the Page 15 Wafer-Thin Explosive Device!* You will feel a bit silly if the Device is detonated by the energy-field of an alien—just as you are creeping up on him—and you are disabled by your own Handbook.

To be on the safe side, therefore, you should devote a few hours each day to making an exact copy of the whole book, in your neatest handwriting.

DEAD BIRO'S

Any type of blank paper will do, but if you can get hold of a large piece of white cloth, so much the better. Your replica Handbook can then be disguised as a sling (see illustration on Page 89), thus providing quick and easy access to its precious, life-saving contents. The sling will also come in handy should either of your arms receive a direct hit from an alien stun-ray.

Next on your equipment-list is a full set of Constellation-Spotter Cards: one for every constellation in the sky. The Spotter who is AAARTHA! will also include the constellations which can only be seen from Australia. In the event of your family deciding to emigrate to Australia, or take a holiday 'Down Under', you will then be in a position to start alien-hunting as soon as you land.

A copy of 2000 A.D. is a good idea. It will identify you to other Spotters, and can also be used as a distress signal, when tied to the tip of your PERISCOPE (See 'Hardware').

Now on to some Hardware. You will need a TELE-SCOPE, of course, to back up your Constellation-Spotter Cards. Spotters who have opted to build one of the giant 'scopes, such as the 154" AAT, will need some form of vehicle to tow it around in. As this could cause problems in heavy traffic, most Spotters will feel more at home with the smaller, cardboard-and-spectacle lens model.

You can be much more adventurous, however, in your choice of a reliable PERISCOPE, essential for observing alien activity at ground level while the Spotter remains unseen.

Bookshops and libraries are bulging with 'guides' which contain instructions on how to build simple working peri scopes out of bits of cardboard, and pocket mirrors. We strongly advise you to forget them. The Spotter who takes a real pride in his work will be content with nothing less than a

NOTE: Trainee Spotters who can't be bothered to equip themselves with a genuine, midget-submarine periscope should refer to APPENDIX B, (page 127) which explains how to build one out or cardboard and pocket mirrors. (ugh!)

genuine *Submarine Periscope*, which has been removed from its conning-tower.

(Our main objection to conning-towers, is that they are rather bulky, and you may not be allowed to travel on buses or trains. This would seriously hamper your movements.)

Periscopes from Nuclear Submarines and U-Boats might also prove to be something of a handicap, in terms of weight and size. But don't let this put you off . . . because there are plenty of second-hand *midget* submarine periscopes about! Small shopkeepers sometimes stock them, and we know of one Spotter who picked up a slightly damaged midget-sub periscope at a Sea Scouts jumble sale. After the rust had been cleaned off, and a dead mouse removed from the eyepiece, it could spot a Pavonian Featherneck at 500 metres.

You could also try your local Navy Surplus Stores. And don't forget to scour your own attic, or boxroom. If you have a relative who served in the Navy during the last world war, there is just a chance that he might have brought home a midget submarine as a souvenir.

Cardboard periscopes may be a lot easier on the pocket,

but they are only suitable for short-range work. The Spotter who takes the time and trouble to equip himself with the real thing, will feel much more AAARTHA!

To be a hundred-percent AAARTHA!, you will also need an efficient COMMUNICATING DEVICE, so that you can link up with other Spotters who may be operating in your area. Two-way radios look very smart, but they are expensive, and vulnerable to interference by alien jammers. Not to mention *human* jammers. There are so many C.B. radio enthusiasts about, these days, that you might find yourself talking to a French 'breaker' from Boulogne, driving a juggernaut of frozen frogs-legs up the M1.

Although radios and suchlike are very glamorous, you will be well advised to go for something that is cheap, easy to maintain, and which gives off a noise which will mean absolutely nothing to the enemy. We are not talking about whistles, or bird noises, or even Viking-type horns.

We are talking about *doors*.

You can hear doors being banged and slammed at almost any hour of the day or night, can't you? Especially *car* doors. Now the world is littered with old, unwanted cars—so you should be able to snap up a decent door for next to nothing. But make sure that it is a *rear* door. Rear doors suffer far less wear-and-tear than front ones, and they seem to close with a much more satisfying KCHUNNK!

All you have to do then is learn the Morse Code, and you

can slam away to your heart's content without having to worry about alerting alien ears. They will simply interpret your signals as a lot of people getting in and out of cars. But take extra care not to catch your fingers in the door. A scream of agony, coming in the middle of your message, will only confuse the Spotter you are trying to communicate with.

Which brings us to the last two items of equipment which should accompany you on every mission. Your stock of tricks and stunts for CREATING AN IMPRESSION OF SUPER-POWER can be concealed in your clothing, or draped around the neck in the case of the Edible Candle (bananas/cucumbers).

And don't forget to take a SURVIVAL PACK. Something to nibble during those long hours of watching and waiting. If weather conditions are bad, a bowl of nourishing stew or a cup of hot soup will work wonders for your confidence. To prepare a hot meal, you will need a primus stove, fuel for the stove, and a collapsible, non-stick frying pan . . .

To sum up, then, the full list of equipment required by the Spotter who is AAARTHA! is as follows;

1. A hand-written Replica of the Handbook, preferably disguised as a sling
2. A complete set of Constellation-Spotter Cards
3. A copy of 2000 A.D.
4. 1 Telescope (plus Towing Vehicle, if using a 154" AAT)
5. 1 Midget-Submarine Periscope
6. 1 Communicating Door
7. Range of Devices for Creating an Impression of Super-Power
8. 1 Survival Pack
9. 1 pair of Wellingtons for Silent Tracking (optional)

It really goes without saying that you should also equip yourself with a notebook and pencil for naking-on-the spot reports.

One might also include a Reserve Survival Pack, money for bus-fares, a compass, a wristwatch, a torch, an umbrella in case it rains, a list of Alien phrases, your A.S.S. identity-

card, a bicycle, a packet of chewing-gum, a transistor radio (so's you don't miss your favourite D.J.), a set of aqualungs (in case you are tracking Aquatic Aliens), a depth-gauge, a photo of your girl-friend/boy-friend, in case you get lonely, three carrier-pigeons, two marker-pens, and a road-map of Clacton-on-Sea (or Birmingham, etc., according to where you live).

Having attired yourself in as much equipment as you consider necessary to feel well and truly AAARTHA!, you should then look something like this.

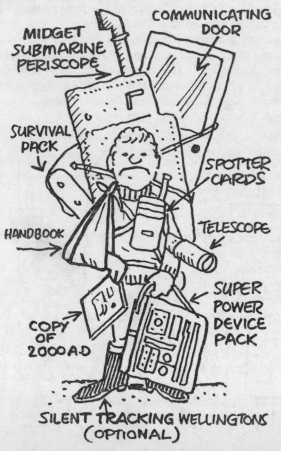

MIDGET SUBMARINE PERISCOPE

COMMUNICATING DOOR

SURVIVAL PACK

SPOTTER CARDS

HANDBOOK

TELESCOPE

COPY OF 2000 A.D

SUPER POWER DEVICE PACK

SILENT TRACKING WELLINGTONS (OPTIONAL)

We know what you are thinking. If one goes wandering around in full hunting-gear, as above, isn't one liable to attract attention?

Perhaps. But if you are the kind of person who is prepared to boldly go where no one has been before, you won't be deterred by the curious glances of passers-by. If anyone questions you about your odd appearance, you will simply raise your eye-brows in amazement, and retort, '*What* periscope?' Or 'I bought it at a car-door sale. Where on earth do you *think* I got it?', and continue on your way with a shake of the head, and a quiet chuckle, as if mildly amused by the strange behaviour of your fellow humans.

Aliens are a different matter, and you may feel that you need some sort of disguise. If so, the Alien Spotter Service is way ahead of you! At this very moment, our scientists are working on a range of disguises which can be worn over your equipment. Yes, the A.S.S. thinks of everything.

The A.S.S. is . . . AAARTHA!

Missing Metamorphs

'Metamorphs' are aliens which specialise in changing their shapes. On this page, and Page 106. (don't you DARE look at Page 106 yet!), are two scenes depicting a group of Metamorphs meeting secretly at a council tip. As a test of your powers of observation, study the scene on this page for one minute, carefully noting the positions and identities of the various aliens . . .

Now turn to Page 106.

Species 077/TQ

Classification:	GRROLMOK MULC-TRUDGER
Origin:	Planetary system of partially-collapsed star in Aquila.
Main Characteristics:	Ammonia-breathing species of low intelligence. Valued for their colossal muscular strength, and almost endless stamina, evolved from constant combat with the ever-present drainage problems of their watery planet. Willing to 'trudge through the mulc' until they drop, these slow-witted creatures command very high salaries in the 'dirty jobs' sector of Grrolmok society.

On Earth, Grrolmoks relish the comparatively low force of gravity, which enables them to run, leap, and propel objects with great power. Tend to masquerade as sportsmen, particularly professional footballers.

All kinds of Aliens

You must have gathered by now that the Earth is infested by a wide variety of super-intelligent, extra-terrestrial beings, armed with a fearsome array of diabolical weapons. So what are they waiting for? If these super-powerful creatures are planning to take over this planet, why on earth don't they get on with it?

The short answer is . . . they are having too much fun!

To many aliens, the Earth is a kind of giant, orbiting 'playground', complete with an endless supply of targets for their mischievous venom. They wouldn't *dream* of spoiling things by conquering it; not just yet, anyway.

And so the chaos continues. Traffic jams, industrial disputes, infuriating losses of sound and vision on the telly, freak weather conditions that make the Earthlings late for work and ruin their holidays. Think of almost any little thing that drives you up the wall, and you can bet your life that aliens are at the bottom of it.

But their love of mischief-making could be their undoing; because it has given the A.S.S. precious time to build up a register of recognisable alien types, based on the particular pranks that they get up to. This enables us to identify an alien which has already possessed an Earthling, or metamorphed into, say, a self-employed plumber.

Once again, we must turn to the constellations, and in particular, the twelve constellations which form the Signs of the Zodiac— ARIES, TAURUS, GEMINI, CANCER, LEO, VIRGO, LIBRA, SCORPIO, SAGITTARIUS, CAPRICORN, AQUARIUS and PISCES.

ZODIACAL QWAX-FAX

The 'Zodiac' is the name given to the band of constellations along which the Sun, Moon, and the planets appear to move. It was devised by Mesopotamian astronomers as early as 3,000 B.C., and is now the basis for modern 'Astrology', which claims that the positions of a planet (relative to a constellation) at the time of a person's birth influences his life, and determines his pattern of behaviour.

Doctor Qwax goes on to suggest that Astrology was actually 'invented' by bogus astronomers, such as Hipparchus and Ptolemy, as a convenient means of coding the 'behaviour' of various alien life-forms, according to the constellations from which they came. In other words, if a *human* trouble-maker behaves in a way which is said to be typical of Capricornians, it is probably due to the fact that he is possessed by an alien from Capricorn. Or a 'typical' Sagittarian might be a shape-changer from Sagittarius.

We can test the accuracy of Dr. Qwax' theory by looking at all the Zodiacal constellations, and checking their 'influences' against some of the infuriating people you must have come across, from time to time.

Take ARIES, for example. Aliens from Aries are creatures of boundless energy and aggression. Brimming with new ideas, they are born leaders; but think only of themselves, and tend to show off a lot. Thus, in *human* form, Arien Aliens can be placed in the following categories.

School bullies who ask for volunteers

Adults who order you about at parties

Disc Jockeys who do impressions

Television Quiz-Show Compères who take a fiendish delight in telling you what you *would* have won if you had answered the last question correctly

Lady Cyclists who accelerate just as motorists are about to overtake them

Teachers who make you go in goal

Aliens from the constellation TAURUS are perhaps the rarest of all ... for they are the strong and silent types. Honest, stolid, and patient. But they can still give you the creeps when disguised as Earthlings such as ...

Boring Opening Batsmen

Successful Burglars

Gardeners who glare at kids in allotments

Quiet Uncles who say 'I've heard it,' after you have told· them your best, and longest joke

Teachers who wait until one full second past the end of the period before dismissing the class.

Sinister Park Keepers

All other people who Keep You Waiting

The CANCER star-group provides a very different kind of alien. He likes to be known as the original 'Nice Guy', and loves to bask in your admiration. But he is apt to be change-able; tends to say one thing, and do another, and can be very peevish and sulky if things don't go right for him. Cancerians can be identified as . . .

Brilliantly Successful Politicians
Milkmen who can Turn Nasty
Grannies who can't get their own way (see 'Is Your Granny an Alien?')
Some Football Club Managers
Do-It-Yourself Dads who never get anything finished (classic case of Alien Possession)

CLASSIC CASE OF ALIEN POSSESSION

SCORPIO sends us aliens with very expensive tastes. They are usually cool, very dignified, and inclined to be ruthless. Watch for humans with the ability to exert power over others, such as . . .

Snooty Traffic-Wardens
Prime Ministers
Teachers who only confiscate Sweets
Well-dressed Hypnotists
Doctors with Cold Hands
Brainy kids who charge a small fee for a peek at their homework.

ABILITY TO WIELD POWER OVER OTHERS

SAGITTARIANS are a particularly irritating species. These friendly, happy-go-lucky aliens are in their element when you are feeling low. Eternally optimistic, they are great animal-lovers, and succeed in making our lives a misery in the following ways . . .

Postmen who whistle merrily as they deliver massive Rate
    Demands, and other household bills
Department store Santa Claus' with smelly breath and
    knobbly knees
Adults who beam and say 'Never mind, eh?' when you are
    dropped from the school team
Next-door neighbours who chuckle, 'He's only being
    friendly,' when their dog goes for you ('animal-lovers')

Television Announcers who smile as they announce that your favourite prog has been cancelled because of an Industrial Dispute

Policemen who make you feel honoured to be arrested

BEWARE SAGITTARIAN ANIMAL LOVERS

Especially adept at driving you round the bend, are aliens from PISCES (pronounced 'Pie-seez'). Being very talkative, they are drawn to the acting profession, but are somewhat deceitful and inclined to exaggerate things. Pisceans like to be part of a team. They are also fascinated by subjects such as Astronomy, and love to travel. If you encounter any of the following human types, it is very likely that you are in the presence of a Piscean Alien . . .

Footballers who pretend that you have fouled them

Most Sports Commentators

Bus Drivers who hurtle past queues, especially when it is raining ('love to travel')

Teachers who insist on taking the best parts in School Drama productions

Girl-friends who talk incessantly about Pop Stars ('fascinated by Astronomy')

Adults who pretend they are useless at draughts/chess/ battleships/video-games, and proceed to wipe the floor with you

The symbol of the 'heavenly twins' gives a clue to the nature of GEMINI aliens, who are rather two-faced. Although on the surface they appear lazy and fun-loving, Geminians are intelligent, charming, and extremely quick-witted. They are also very quick to find fault, and never look their age. Spotters should be very wary of:

Chatty, jovial doctors who scoff at the suggestion that you are too ill to attend school

Teachers who thump you before you can explain that you were actually trying to knock a wasp of the new kid's cap ('quick to find fault')

Showbiz stars selected for 'This is Your Life' who pretend that it's all a Big Surprise

Horribly-injured footballers who perform cartwheels when their team is awarded a penalty

Gigantic sporting opponents

Dads who read the Sunday Telegraph in bed ('intelligent but lazy')

In sharp contrast to Geminians, aliens from the constellation LEO are reputed to be strong, lordly, and dignified. The typical Leo is a born leader, who usually speaks his mind, and, although good-natured, is often very haughty and indifferent to the feelings of others. Well-built and active, Leo subjects make few close friends, for the following reasons:

Adults who stand on your feet in supermarkets
Mums who make you help them with the shopping
Kids who won't lend you anything
Visiting uncles with bone-scrunching handshakes
Sporting superstars who refuse to give autographs
Fast, powerful teachers who reach your desk before you
can hide the comic you have been reading ('Well-built
and active')

VIRGO aliens are equally aggravating, even though they are supposed to be modest, and reserved. Virgoans have excellent memories, and can be relied on to remain cool, calm and collected, even when all about them are going potty. Inquisitive and questioning by nature, they are very fussy about food, and exhibit a tremendous interest in history, and historical things. Prime examples of aliens from Virgo are:

Girl-friends who want to know *exactly* why you were five
minutes late
Adults who remember that you have promised faithfully
to do something boring
Teachers who criticise your cookery skills ('fussy about
food')
Smooth disco-dancers ('remain cool and calm when all
about them are going potty')
Elderly disc-jockeys, and all their fans ('interest in
historical things')

The symbol of LIBRA is the 'scales', so it is not surprising that Librans are well-balanced, harmonious, and fair-minded. Drawn to beautiful things, they tend to be artistic, and consider themselves expert judges of talent and fashion. Although they love to argue, our charming and witty Librans will soon win you over. Keep a sharp look-out for:

Dads who insist on watching the Miss Universe contest when there's football on the other channel

Footballers who execute a quick performance of Swan Lake after scoring a goal ('tend to be artistic')

Folk-singers who never fall off their stools ('harmonious and well-balanced')

Teachers who make you feel honoured to receive extra homework

Parents who disagree when you claim that you have just brushed your teeth ('love to argue')

Adults who are appalled by the way you dress ('judges of fashion')

Aliens who gather under the sign of CAPRICORN, the 'sea-goat', are particularly difficult to pin down. Typical Capricornians are said to be withdrawn, gloomy, jealous, and obsessed with impending doom. Yet they are skilled public speakers, and have a strong feeling for music. Once he embarks on something, the Capricornian will see it through to the bitter end. Interested in all sorts of weird subjects, such as the Supernatural, he can be a loyal and devoted friend. But beware! The following types are *anything* but friendly:

People who creep up behind you and go 'BOO!' (interested in ... the Supernatural')

Sports commentators who make funny whistling noises ('public speakers with a feeling for music')

Kids who won't share their sweets

Parents who make you eat all your dinner, even the cabbage

Elderly relatives who think the world is coming to an end

Girls who go out with you because your brother has got a 500 c.c. Yamaha ('loyal and devoted friend')

Last, but by no means least, the aliens of AQUARIUS rank high in the league of mischief-makers. Apparently kind,

understanding, helpful and sympathetic, their quiet manner conceals an inner strength and forcefulness. Don't be fooled by their gentle ways. Aquarians who profess to a love of peace and quiet betray their darker instincts in the following ways:

School bullies who help you up so's they can knock you
　　down again
Teachers who give you detention so that you can finish
　　your homework ('kind and understanding')
Gentle doctors with ticklish hands
Parents who never listen to what you're saying ('a love of
　　peace and quiet')
Old ladies who drag you out of seats in crowded buses
Sympathetic central defenders who apologise for kicking
　　you over the crossbar

Quite a parade of aggravating aliens, isn't it? As an exercise in Alien Identification, study all the Zodiacal signs, and their basic characteristics, and see if they apply to any adults or kids who have been making a nuisance of themselves, just lately.

But don't confine your researches to the Zodiacal constellations. In the night sky, Taurus is a neighbour of Auriga (The Charioteer), so if you know of a Boring Opening Batsman (see Taurean types, above) who drives a chariot, he might be a Taurean Alien who has done a tour of duty in Auriga. You can pinpoint quite a number of alien sub-species in this way, but make sure that you use one of the Zodiacal constellations as a starting point.

But never forget that the main danger comes from the Big Twelve. And once we have learned to identify these alien mischief-makers in all their infuriating forms, there is only one way to deal with them—be patient! Keep your head, and refuse to be infuriated.

Once your tormentor realises that his tactics aren't working, he will become more and more demoralised Eventually, his superiors will pronounce him unfit for duty and he will be withdrawn to his home planet.

You have won another round in the fight to Save the Earth

NOTE: Aliens use calender-systems which are completely different from ours, which means that newspaper 'Horoscopes' are of little use in checking the accuracy of your identification. Even so, many Earthlings are possessed by aliens whose Zodiacal 'signs' match the date of birth of their victims, e.g. 'Libra' (Sept 23—Oct 23)'. This gives rise to such remarks as 'He's a typical Libran, he is!', thus encouraging modern Astrologers in the belief that the Signs of the Zodiac were devised by Earthlings.

In the case of Shape-Changers, dates of birth are meaningless Alien Metamorphs usually fib about their date of birth, anyway— especially the female of the species.

Missing Metamorphs

The scene is the same, except that three of the Aliens have changed themselves into bits of rubbish. Without looking back at Page 91, can you identify the missing Metamorphs?

Answers on page 128.

A Spot of Indoor Practice

Just because there may be a lull in alien activity, or it is raining cats and dogs*, it doesn't mean to say that you can take a break from training. The work of the Spotter is never done.

Fortunately, the A.S.S. has devised a fascinating little game which will help you to carry on Saving the Earth, even when you are stuck indoors. It is called 'Construct a Creature', and can be played by two, or four Spotters, depending on the number of colleagues who are stuck indoors with you.

All you need are some sheets of blank paper, a supply of biros or pencils, and a vivid imagination. Having tossed a coin to decide who goes first, one of the players proceeds to sketch the head of an alien being at the top of a sheet of paper, in such a way that the other players cannot see what he is drawing.

The paper is then folded, so that only the lower edge of the alien's neck is visible. This is the starting point for the second player, who adds the torso and arms of the figure.

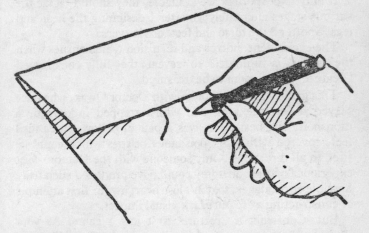

* Such weather may itself be evidence of alien activity. See 'Showers of Frogs and Toads', page 42.

The legs of our imaginary alien are provided by a third player, while the fourth player completes the picture with a pair of highly-imaginative feet. The paper is folded at every stage, so that the various body-sections remain a complete mystery to at least three of the players.

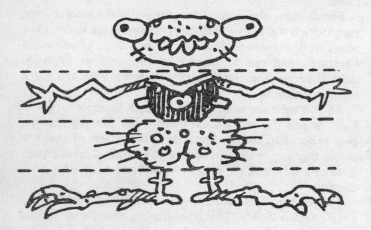

If only two Spotters are available, they should tackle the various stages alternately; Spotter 1 designing the head and legs, Spotter 2 the torso and feet, or vice versa.

The excitement, horror and revulsion which ensues when the paper is unfolded to reveal the fully-constructed Creature, is a moment to be treasured.

This game was very popular with Doctor Qwax, who once played it for weeks on end whilst trapped indoors by a monsoon. His best effort was a pair of yellow, three-toed feet, covered with long, poisonous bristles which could be fired in all directions. Only someone with the Doctor's vast experience of alien anatomy could have produced such truly horrible appendages; so don't lose heart if your first attempts at constructing a creature lack visual impact.

But 'Construct a Creature' isn't just a game. As your designs, through constant practise, take on Qwax-like flair and audacity, there is always the chance that you and your

fellow-spotters will hit upon something which bears a close resemblance to a 'Thing from Outer Space' which has just scared the daylights out of a member of the public.

Remove it instantly to your personal register of Alien Life-Forms, and file under the section marked 'New Species; Sighting Confirmed'.

Then give yourself a resounding pat on the back, and celebrate with another round of 'Construct a Creature'. You have proved that the dedicated Spotter can function under the most adverse conditions, even when he is stuck indoors, and there is nothing on the telly.

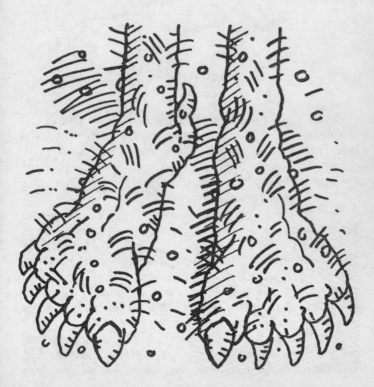

Alien Sky-Jackers

Dr. Qwax, being quite rich, has personally financed the construction of a system of satellites and probes which are designed to detect approaching alien space-craft. The following scenes are reproductions of two photographs taken by one of these satellites, just before it was stolen by the crew of a Vulgan battle-cruiser.

The second photograph, taken a split-second after the first, shows ten subtle imperfections, caused by radiation from the battle-cruiser's engines. Can you find them?

Answers on page 128.

Species 111/TQ

Classification:	ANTAREAN KADETTE
Origin:	Elite City-World of Antares, in the constellation Scorpius.
Main Characteristics:	The subject featured is only 13 Earth years old; the age at which the Antarean Kadette reaches a peak of intelligence and artistic ability. Then follows a steady, intellectual decline, until honoured retirement at the age of 28. Spotters are recommended to look for 'Child Prodigies', such as children who can solve Rubik Cube-type puzzles at irritating speed, for evidence of A.K. (Antarean Kadette) possession.

PROFITS

Cosmic Chit-Chat

Apart from the Betelgeusian phrases kindly revealed to us by Tharg, the A.S.S. is currently compiling a dictionary of Extra-terrestrial Language, gleaned from bugging devices placed at strategic points. Some of the more important alien phrases are listed below. Memorise them, and note down any other words or phrases that you may overhear.

Bus queues; pop concerts, discos, football matches, political rallies, and crowded supermarkets are good places to eavesdrop. Aliens love to lapse into their own language—if they think no one else is listening—because it reminds them of home.

HARJ!	Hello
JYK! JYK!	Goodbye!
ZARK-LAX MKOSH!	I arrived last Tuesday
VLEN UIST ARL NOJ-QUIRN DRRT?	Have you change for a ten quirn note?
Y-MI TRAG CHOOMIN KU SLYTHERKRIN	I am thinking of changing my Earthling.
YANKUM KWIK?	American Express?
KU GLULT-MUNGE JEL JANTLEMIK	My glult (food) parcel is overdue.
VRAAAR!	Goal!
GRI D VESNEG KNOTTIG OYX-MOYX JUNFA!	Off-side!
AVAL YEECCH?	With chips?
ZOM KOPPLEGRI VLEN TURRNDI-WYRN KU PTROONJUTTLE!	The Police have towed away my spaceship.
Y-MI HISTO-ZONDHIK BROLZ	I am a hundred-and-seventy-nine today.
KLIRJ CALLAKUM-DIMOK	Many Happy Returns!
KU BZAT—NATTEN JEL D GRAGGASPLYT	My laser-gun is on the sideboard.
UIST-DRIJ NOR DES O'CONNOR?	Do you know Des O'Connor?

NUKK! RUL-TIG DINNIT, Y SWYDOK-KU JEL D ZYRKAFONE* ZLEET-HAFF D RIFFLE-ZIZ?	No. But if you hum it, I will follow you on the Zyrkafone. Where is the nearest Time-Warp?
DER ZLAK-LI BNUN WOOLWORTHS, RUL ZOM KOPPLEGRI VLEN TURRNDI-WYRNDI.	There was one behind Woolworths, but the Police have towed it away.

It would be impossible, of course, to compile a dictionary of all the extra-terrestrial languages which are spoken throughout the Galaxy. The above phrases are based on a 'universal' dialect developed by the various life-forms which have visited this planet.

The aliens call it 'Earth-Speak'.

* A type of Merakian guitar.

Close Encounters

Hardly a day passes without someone—somewhere in the world—claiming that he or she has seen a UFO, or established contact with a Being from Another World.

With a few exceptions, these so-called 'Close Encounters' can be safely ignored. Many of them have been exposed by A.S.S. investigators as the work of hoaxsters; while such everyday objects as aircraft, meteors, satellites, and weather balloons have inspired a host of nonsensical stories about visiting spacecraft, and little green men.

While we do not dispute the fact that there are aliens which are small in stature, and as green as Kermit the Frog, some of the following sightings must be taken with a pinch of salt.

But others have the hard ring of truth, and, in our humble opinion, provide irrefutable proof that aliens are alive and well, and living on this planet.

First, let us make sure that the meaning of the expression 'Close Encounter' is fully understood. There are three main categories:

Close Encounter of the FIRST Kind (C.E.1)
> Any sighting of an Unidentified Flying Object (UFO), not involving physical contact, but which may affect the witness in some way (e.g. bulging eyes, knocking knees, sweaty armpits, weird buzzing noises on observer's trannie).

Close Encounter of the SECOND Kind (C.E.2)
> Any sighting of an Extraterrestrial Being, not involving physical contact.

Close Encounter of the THIRD Kind (C.E.3)
> ACTUAL PHYSICAL CONTACT with an Extraterrestrial Being.

Encounters of the Fourth Kind and upwards usually result in the disappearance or liquidation of the observer, so we can

ignore them for the purposes of this chapter.

We were also tempted to ignore the following report, submitted by Miss Deborah Allsop of Twyford, Hants, who claims to have experienced a C.E.1 in March, 1978. According to an entry in Deborah's diary:

the whole sky was crammed with space ships, and their pilots must have been ever so cheecky, cos they kept landing and taking off every few minutes.
Each ufo was gitted with lots of flashing, colourd lights, and you never heard such a roaring and rumbling sound.

I bet I could even remember the exact time it all happend cos we were seeing our gran off from London airport.

Obviously a Close Encounter of the Highly-Imaginative Kind!

Still on the subject of spacecraft, take a look at this photograph of a UFO, taken through this bedroom window by 11 year-old Malcolm Timberlake of Wakefield, Yorks. He was using a Palimex 35mm camera, set at f.11 aperture, with a shutter speed of one sixtieth of a second:

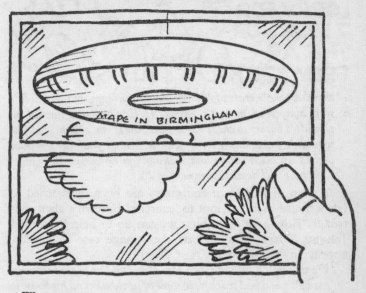

We are not sure what to make of this one. The words 'Made in Birmingham', printed on the hull of the craft, could be an attempt by the aliens to put us off the scent. Malcolm has always hotly denied that the UFO is actually a plastic, British Home Stores lampshade, hanging just inside his bedroom window. A.S.S. experts are still investigating the incident.

But there seems no reason to doubt the word of 8 year-old Isla MacNulty of Perth, Scotland, who claims to be the victim of a particularly bizarre C.E.3, in that her Jack Russell terrier, Edward, is possessed by an alien:

My Edward used to be a nice, playful, barking sort of dog, but now he keeps chasing things. First it was people, then cyclists, and then he started galloping after milk-floats. Our milkman

EDWARD JUST AFTER CHASING A LORRY FOR 7 MILES UP THE A9 FROM PERTH → PHEW

threw a whole crate of Moosly Yoghurt at him, but that didn't stop him. And now it's lorries. If Edward was normal he wouldn't bother to chase lorries, because if you caught one, you wouldn't know what to do with it, would you? So I reckon there's an alien inside him making him do these silly things. I suppose it'll be airplanes next . . .'

A team of A.S.D. investigators has been despatched to Isla's house in an attempt to 'exorcise' Edward's alien controller. But there is nothing we can do to help 9 year-old Johnny Norris, who reports the strange case of his disappearing form-master:

'We were all a bit sad when Mr. Perry told us he was retiring, 'cos he's not a bad teacher, so some of us went round his house to wish him good luck. Just as we got there, a fantastic beam of light shone down into a field near Mr. Perry's house. And there was Mr. Perry, standing at the bottom of the beam. But not for long. Bit by bit he slowly disappeared, until there was nothing left. What got me is that our class had a whip round for him, and bought him a new squash racket, and now it's gone. What a waste of good pocket-money . . .'

There is little doubt that the bogus Mr. Perry was an alien shape-changer, and that Johnny saw him being beamed up at the end of his tour of duty; armed with the squash racket which he had so cruelly prised out of his pupils.

As Johnny was once thumped by Mr. Perry (physical contact) for scrumping apples from the school kitchen garden, this must count as a C.E.3.

This account of an alien who went up, leads us neatly into a C.E.1 sighting involving aliens who came down. This reproduction of a photograph taken by the best friend of Betty Pugh, shows Betting posing beside the 'scorch-marks' left by a fleet of alien ships, which she claims, landed in a field in Aberystwyth, in 1969:

In her report, Betty states:
'... *the ships must have landed between midnight and dawn, because there was a funfair in the field the previous night, and my mate Karen went on the dodgems with Terry Andrews, but they didn't see any UFOs*...'

We are not surprised that Karen and Terry didn't see anything; apart from marquees, and shooting-ranges, and carousels, which leave similar marks in fields when they are moved on to another site.

Full marks to Betty Pugh for trying, although she clearly allowed her imagination to run riot; as did 7 year-old Brian Digweed of Shepton Mallett. Brian, it seemed was the sole spectator of a searing battle between rival fleets of alien starships:

It seemed to go on for ars one of the spaseships was over three mile long it sent out lotts of littul shipps witch ataked the enemi. i kno they wer usin deth rays cos the heet of the batle was so strong i got horribli berned an had to put sum laster plast on mi nose wen i got home. i am goin too sea STAR WARS agen toomorow an this tyme it wil seame evun mor relistik cos i ave sean the horror of it wiv mi own eies

We suspect that Brian's injury was caused by a lamp post which collided with his nose as he wandered along, staring at the sky, shortly after his visit to the above-mentioned movie.

And so it is to Titchwell, Norfolk, that we must now turn our attention for evidence of a truly sensational, and *genuine*, C.E.3—the harrowing capture and torture of 13 year-old Vivian Bowyer, by the crew of an extra-terrestrial ship.

One evening in September, 1981, Vivian was returning from a disco at her local school, when she observed a tall, silvery figure standing in the middle of the road. As the shape lifted its right arm, and aimed a slender, wand-like instrument at her, Vivian's nightmare began:

'... *my bicycle-lamp exploded, both tyres punctured, and my Cliff Richard L.P. burst into song, so I knew that something unusual was happening. Then everything went black. When I opened my eyes again, I was lying on a sort of slab inside a dome-shaped chamber which I took to be the interior of a space-ship, like what you see in Star Trek. The silvery thing that pointed the wand at me was standing in a corner, along with three others, doing something with my L.P. Suddenly, the gentle vibes of Cliff, singing 'Livin' Doll' wafted through the chamber. As the aliens listened in spellbound amazement, I was able to sneak past them, and find my way out of the ship. Then I just ran, and ran, and ran, as fast as my legs could carry me...'*

By the time Vivian returned to the spot, an hour later, in her father's car, the alien ship had vanished, along with her L.P.; but Vivian is convinced that the disc saved her life. She has since become a Trainee Spotter, and is trying to persuade the A.S.S. to add the works of Mr. Cliff Richard to the range of essential, alien-hunting equipment, described in the chapter entitled 'AAARTHA!'

Let us all wish her the best of luck.

We conclude this motley collection of Close Encounters with yet another case of abduction by aliens; this time, involving animals.

The unfortunate human observer of the incident—which seems chillingly authentic—was one Arnold Hedgethicket, the simple, hardworking son of a Cornish cowman.

Only a few months ago, Arnold was sketching wild-life in a corner of a cowfield at Sugget's Farm, Marazion, when in his own words:

'...oi 'eard a noise loike a washing-machine, zumwhere up in the skoi. Aar, I thought... that be one o' them there 'elicopter jobs. But it weren't. It were a gert big, bluey-grey thing, shaped loike one o' Missus Sugget's pudden bowls. It just sat there for a bit, 'overin over the cowfield, an then 'e let out a sort o' buzzin noise, which made moi 'air stand ter attention. It were just then that the cows started takin orf. First Daisy, then Betsy, wi the rest roight behind 'em. Ole Freda put up a bit o' a struggle loike, but then she took orf, too. Last oi saw on 'em, they were driftin up through a big ole in the bottom o' the pudden-bowl. Oi were a bit kermuzzled, oi can tell 'e. Oi mean, it bein't every day that you sees a whole herd o' proize cows sailin' orf loike a load o' 'elicopters...'

Poor Arnold. He didn't know then that he had witnessed an alien 'zoo' ship collecting a few more specimens, with the aid of an anti-grav beam.

But Farmer Sugget may not have to wait very long for the return of his cattle. Remember the Frogs that deluged an American golf course, in 1973? If the crew of that alien zoo-ship are equally careless, we may wake up one morning, and see the following headlines in the national press:

So watch the skies . . . KEEP WATCHING!

At any time now, Farmer Sugget's stolen herd may come hurtling from the heavens. And if you have the misfortune to be standing underneath it, you will join the ranks of those who have experienced the shock and terror of a genuine CLOSE ENCOUNTER.

The A.S.S. would like to hear from you.

Dr. Qwax: the Final Message

This Handbook would not be complete without a last word from the man who made it all possible. Several last words, in fact. They were transmitted to A.S.S. Headquarters via the microscopic radio that Dr. Qwax smuggled into the amusement arcade, in dogged pursuit of the Alien Mastermind which he had hunted for so long.

In a hushed voice, he can be heard taking stock of his surroundings:

'... *Ah-hah! Looks as if they've just installed a new video-game... 'Laser Wars'. Haven't played that one before, so I'll have a quick go on it ... just in case I'm being, er ... watched, you understand. Here we go then ... Hmm! Interesting programming ... Thrust button ... hyper-jump facility ... bonus points if you can zap ... I-I mean, destroy that big, vibrating yellow thing. Oooops! Nearly got one of my laser-bases ... but I'm getting the hang of it now! Take that, you little fiends! ... and that! ... and THAT! I've almost obliterated a whole squadron! Hee! Heeeeee! They'll never outwit me! Never, never, never ... AAAAAAAAHHHHH! ...*'

A.S.S. investigators are still puzzling over the meaning of that final, anguished cry, which brings the transmission to an abrupt halt. Did the radio develop a fault? Had the Doctor's hitherto, razor-sharp vigilance relaxed in the excitement of the game, allowing the Alien Mastermind to overpower him? Or was he upset because one of his laser-bases had been zapped by the big yellow thing?

Perhaps we shall never know. All we can do is make sure that his sacrifice was not in vain, by hunting down the inhuman menace that lurks in every corner of our society.

Starting with that amusement arcade, wherever it is ..

Appendix A

Thankfully, the alien battleship mentioned in 'Scope for Improvement' has been driven off. An A.S.S. scrambler-beam has caused its computerised weapons-system to malfunction, and there is now no need to build an Anti Flesh-Shredding Gamma-Cannon Shelter.

Instead, here is another little trick which may save your life if you are careless enough to fall into the slimy hands of an alien sabotage-squad.

Ask one of the aliens to think of *any number below 10*. Then ask him (or better still, *instruct* him in a commanding voice) to multiply the number by 5, add 7, and then double the answer (without telling you, of course).

Then, gazing mysteriously at the other aliens, choose the one with his mouth (or mouths) open, and instruct him to whisper another number—also below 10—to the *first* alien, in such a way that you cannot possibly hear it.

Now tell the *first* alien to add this number to his mental sum (arrived at, remember, by multiplying the number HE thought of by 5, adding 7, and doubling the answer). The first alien is then asked to inform you of the Grand Total.

Still with us? Good. You can now astound the whole, gruesome crew *by revealing both of the numbers which were thought of by the two aliens*!

Yes, we agree that it is a little difficult to follow, but it works, honestly!

For instance, if the FIRST alien thinks of, say, 7, you get the following calculation . . .

$7 \times 5 + 7 = 42$

Double the answer, and you get 84.

Now suppose the SECOND alien thinks of, say, 3, this is added to the FIRST alien's total, making 87, which is the Grand Total that the aliens reveal to you.

All you do then, is subtract 14 from 87 . . .

Ulp! Sorry about that. We forgot to mention that you must always subtract 14 from the aliens' Grand Total; which gives you, er 73. And there you are!

The tens figure (in this case 7) is *always* the number thought of by the FIRST alien; while the second figure (3), is always the number thought of by the SECOND alien.

Simple, eh?

Take any combination of two numbers below 10; follow the sequence of calculations described above, and you cannot fail to accomplish what will appear to be a staggering feat of mind-reading.

There's just one snag. The aliens may be so impressed, they will ask you to do it with numbers which are greater than 10—in which case it may be best to employ some other means of impressing them—such as making yourself invisible.

NOTE: If, indeed, you have mastered the Secret of Invisibility, please do not make yourself invisible, and rush straight round to your nearest A.S.S. Control Centre, because the Controller is very busy, and he won't be able to see you.

Appendix B

For those of you who are determined to build a boring old PERISCOPE, out of cardboard and pocket mirrors, and thus settle for second best, here is how to go about it.

You will need a piece of stiff card, measuring about 30 x 20cm (12″ x 18″), and two small mirrors, about 6cm (2½″) square.

Using a pencil, divide the card along its length into four panels of equal width and cut two square holes as shown.

Near the end of the other two panels, cut four slits at an angle of 458. These are to hold the mirrors in position.

Now bend the card into a rectangular tube, secure the joints with sticky tape,

and slide the mirrors into the slits.

Your home-made, second-rate, second-best, boring old periscope is now ready for use.

Make sure that you place the mirrors at the correct angle, or all you will see is a reflection of yourself.

Answers

FIND THE LEADERS (*Page 16*)
A and F are identical.

SPOTTER IN A SPOT (*Page 51*)
Tunnel 1.

FUNNY PEOPLE, THESE EARTHLINGS (*Page 57*)
1. Dustbins 2. A football match 3. A petrol pump
4. A heat of 'It's a Knock-out' 5. A bingo session.

PLACE THE PORCUPODS (*Page 65*)
There are 8 Porcupods hidden aboard the ship.

CARELESS CREATURES (*Page 68*)
The policeman's ears, the lollipop lady's leg,
the vicar's hand, the boy's tongue, the window cleaner's tail,
the dog's head.

A CODE THAT GETS RESULTS (*Page 82*)
The message reads: MY UNCLE HAS WEBBED FEET.

MISSING METAMORPHS (*Pages 91 & 106*)
Three Metamorphs have turned into a bicycle, a TV set,
and a wheel.

ALIEN SKY-JACKERS (*Pages 110 & 111*)
On page 111: stripe missing on tail of spaceship;
moon is only quarter-full; stud missing in bottom left-hand
corner of satellite window; island missing on planet Earth;
extra finger on alien's left hand; his tail is missing;
one alien has disappeared; one alien's lifeline is missing;
spoke missing from satellite dish; another moon has
appeared in top right hand corner.

The Alien-spotter's Handb

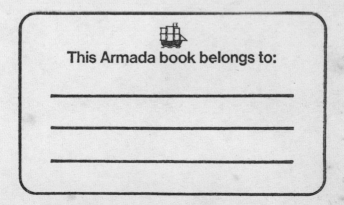

🚢
This Armada book belongs to:

_____

_____

_____